The Second Coming:
An Explanation for the Perplexed

Millennial Mind Publishing
An imprint of American Book Publishing
5442 So. 900 East, #146
Salt Lake City, UT 84117-7204
www.american-book.com
Printed in the United States of America on acid-free paper.

The Second Coming: An Explanation for the Perplexed

Designed by Ahmadullah Emad, design@american-book.com

Publisher's Note: This is a work of fiction. Names, characters, places, and incidents either are the product of the author's imagination, or are used fictitiously, and any resemblance to actual persons, living or dead, events, or locales is entirely coincidental.

ISBN-13: 978-1-58982-519-2
ISBN-10: 1-58982-519-5

Special Sales

These books are available at special discounts for bulk purchases. Special editions, including personalized covers, excerpts of existing books, and corporate imprints, can be created in large quantities for special needs. For more information e-mail info@american-book.com.

The Second Coming:
An Explanation for the Perplexed

Richard E. Stabile

Table of Contents

Introduction

We are about to begin a journey together that will change us. It all began in July, 2003, in the ancient city of Babylon, Iraq. Something very strange happened to me in Babylon, and as you will find out, I'm not good at keeping anything to myself. (They called me "Cable News Joy" in high school.) So I've written this book about it.

My experience is something everyone should go through and have the chance to feel as I did—strangely liberated. To accept what you learn, the process must be the same; a slow revelation that can be both enjoyable and liberating.

I was sent to Babylon, Iraq to work on the reconstruction of the country after the overthrow of Saddam Hussein. Before we start, here are some things you should know about Babylon:

Jerusalem, 586 BC

(I knew this before I went to Babylon, Iraq.)

A king named Zedekiah was twenty-one years old when he began his rule over Judah, in the city of Jerusalem. In the ninth year of his reign, a great army from Babylon surrounded his city. Zedekiah took all of his men of war and fled to the plains of Jericho. There, he was overtaken by the Babylonians, his army scattered from him, and Zedekiah was captured and bound in fetters. The young king was forced to watch the execution of his two sons, and then his eyes were gouged out. (The Iraqis are descendants of the Babylonians. That made me feel just great about going to Iraq!)

The Babylonians entered Jerusalem and burned down the temple and

all the houses of Jerusalem, including the king's palace. Most of the people were taken to Babylon as captives[1].
Babylon, 586 BC

The people of Jerusalem were taken to the City of the Gate of Gold, Babylon. Fifty-six miles of brick wall, three hundred feet high and twenty-five feet thick, surrounded the City of the Gate of Gold. Eight massive gates led to the inner city, where another one hundred brass gates stood. The great temple of the god Marduk was at the center of the city. Another fifty-two temples and one hundred eighty altars to the goddess Ishtar were scattered about the great city, in addition to a golden image of the god Baal and the golden table in the House of the Oracle, which together contained at least forty-four thousand pounds of solid gold[2].

Two golden lions, the symbols of Babylon, and an eighteen-foot-high, solid gold, human-like figure stood within the city. (The Babylonians liked gold.) The king of Babylon, King Nebuchadnezzar, had a magnificent palace at the southern end of the city[3].

Remember that word—GOLD!

The Beginning

Navy Seabees attached to the First Marine Expeditionary Force were the first to reach Babylon during the Iraq War. When they arrived, the city's museum and ruins had already been looted and damaged. The Seabees built Camp Babylon around the city. Polish soldiers guarded the perimeter[4].

I arrived here two months after the Seabees. My mission was to assist in setting up phone banks, Internet access, and electrical communications for Camp Babylon, and to link them to the Air Force base in Tallil, Iraq. Later, I was commissioned to work on establishing links to Karbala, Al Sahra, and Balad. I know that sounds boring. It's what electrical engineers do, though. My sister, June, who is a CPA, does tax returns. *That's* boring!

The second day I was there, I saw Jewish Marines celebrating the Sabbath on the banks of the Euphrates River. Babylon had become a center of Jewish study after the people of Jerusalem were brought there in 586 BC, but, in 2003, there were more Jewish Marines than the number of Jews living in all of Iraq[5]. As a genuine trivia nerd (I have a T-shirt that says "Trivia Nerd" on the back and on both sleeves, and a matching "Trivia Nerd" baseball cap I wear with it), I found that interesting.

Watching the Marines, I was unaware my next day in Iraq would change my life forever.

The next afternoon I went on a walking tour of the ruins of Babylon with my new co-workers, Ricky Elliot and Lisa Sanchez. They had also arrived yesterday, from Miami. Walking next to them never helped my self-esteem. Lisa's beautiful, long, dark brown hair would sway elegantly on her shoulders. It was soft and shiny, and matched her eyes, which always seemed bright with intelligence. My hair was dyed strawberry blond, and cut like Cleopatra's. Can you imagine Cleopatra with dyed, strawberry blond hair? Ricky looked intelligent too, like a young college professor. Together they looked like swinging jet setters, and then there was me, Joy DiNardo; Cleopatra with dyed strawberry-blond hair.

A young Marine that everyone called "Scoot" escorted us on our tour of the ruins. It was weird to keep saying "Scoot." "OK, Scoot." "Thanks, Scoot." "Lead the way, Scoot." "Scoot," to me, normally means "leave," "get away." For some reason, Scoot thought it meant that he was "quick, like a cat." He seemed to like his nickname. He carried an M16, which he pointed at different objects as we walked through old Babylon.

Saddam Hussein had begun to rebuild Babylon before the war. A huge portrait of Saddam and King Nebuchadnezzar hung at the entrance to the ruins. Saddam had rebuilt the walls of Nebuchadnezzar's palace, as well as some temples, gates, and an amphitheater. A museum, gift shop, café, and a magnificent palace had also been added to the city[4,7].

Saddam had built directly over the ruins, so some of the old, authentic sites were destroyed. Many of the bricks used in the reconstruction were inscribed with praises to Saddam: "*This was built by Saddam Hussein, son of Nebuchadnezzar, to glorify Iraq*[7]." Scoot told us that a lot of the bricks had been stolen and were being sold in Europe as souvenirs.

The ruins of Babylon were just that; ruins, consisting mainly of mounds of dirt, broken mud-brick buildings, and debris[6]. That was all that remained of the City of the Gate of Gold. All fifty-three temples and the forty-four thousand pounds of solid gold statues were gone. Some irregular paths could be made out among the ruins that looked like the remnants of streets. I remembered reading that the Babylonians threw their garbage into the streets, and I mentioned this to Scoot. His face scrunched up in disgust, and he said "It figures."

The four of us walked through the ruins as if in a cemetery. I felt peaceful and serene, vaguely noticing the people around us.

A barren plain opened up at the end of the ruins. When we arrived at that point, the four of us stood in silence, staring out at the plain. The solitude of the area seemed to put us into a trance. My brain just wanted to focus on the nothingness that was in front of us---- the never-ending barren plain[6].

"That's where they built the Tower of Babel." Scoot's sort of high-pitched voice penetrated my brain. Tower of Babel? I knew that story. God, angry because some people tried to build a tower to heaven, crushed the tower and made everyone speak different languages. That way, they couldn't cooperate anymore and build another tower to heaven. I guess that was the way the ancients explained why people spoke different languages. Just an old myth. I laughed out loud at Scoot's remark—Tower of Babel—Ha! Who could ever believe such a story?

"You do not believe the story of Babel?" asked someone with a thick Iraqi accent. I turned to see where that question came from. My eyes focused on the stomach area of a person, and then rose up and up and up. A giant stood before us, at least seven feet tall! The giant wore his beard long, trimmed into the shape of a rectangle. He looked ancient but not old, if that makes any sense. He had brown hair (not gray), smile lines and wrinkles around very large eyes, and skin that was weathered, but not tanned; more pale that the average Iraqi. His long tunic touched the ground, making him look like a big statue.

"Old One, where did you come from?" Scoot asked. Lisa had backed away, and I heard Ricky say "eh aw," or something strange like that. He sounded like a donkey. We had acted like the Three Stooges. Scoot explained that "Old One," as he called him, had worked in the museum before it was looted. He was one of the Iraqis that the Marines allow on the base.

Old One continued to stare at me, waiting for a response. That made me nervous, and my neck became stiff from anxiety. My brain sent a message to me—*say something!*

"Um, no, I don't believe the story of Babel."

Now everyone was staring at me in silence. If there had been any crickets chirping in the desert, we would have heard them.

Old One looked insulted. Another minute went by in silence. Old One now appeared to be deeply hurt. I thought, maybe I should consider taking it back; like OK, maybe it could have happened. There must be some part of the story that is true.

"I can teach you the truth," he said finally. "You may be worthy of it."

Worthy of it? What did he mean by that? Everyone stood there awkwardly for another minute. I glanced at Ricky and Lisa. They were standing perfectly still. Ricky looked like he was standing at attention, maybe because Old One was so towering and overwhelming.

For some reason, I just blurted out a word again. "OK."

OK? What a stupid answer that was! OK?

Old One spoke again in a grave voice, "You will have to learn in small amounts. For now, determine why gold is the most valuable. When you know the answer, look for me again."

He began to turn and walk away. Gold? I knew that.

"Wait, um, sir! Gold is valuable because it is a rare, precious metal. That's easy."

Old One stopped, shaking his head and replying, "No. Do not answer without using your abilities." Then he walked away faster.

Why was that the wrong answer, and what did gold have to do with anything? What did gold have to do with the Truth and the Tower of Babel? Who was this guy, anyway? Old One.

Gold

I am a bookworm. I love to look up information and bury myself in books and the Internet, especially when I feel challenged. Some Iraqi giant named Old One had just given me a challenge. At least I think that's what he did. Hmm. Find out why gold is the most valuable. The most valuable what?

I couldn't wait to get back to my room and log onto the Internet on my laptop. Ricky and Lisa told me to forget about it. The conversation was too weird. Scoot said the guy was probably crazy, driven insane by living under Saddam Hussein. The problem is that I have been challenged—I can't just forget about it now.

The Navy Seabees had set up an Internet café in Saddam's palace. I went straight to my room, grabbed my laptop, and made a beeline there. I logged on, and suddenly felt relaxed because I was doing something familiar---- surfing the Web. I always feel relaxed when I am focused on something, like I was back in an engineering class at Penn State.

Let's see, the exact words of Old One, the old goat-looking giant (I know, sometimes I'm juvenile, even though I'm twenty-nine), were *determine why gold is the most valuable*. OK, gold Web sites. I tried this one, "Important dates in the history of gold," and wrote down some of the more interesting ones:

AD 1969: Gold-coated visors protect the astronauts' eyes from searing sunlight on the Moon (That's weird. Why would they use gold? Those were expensive visors!)

AD 1922: King Tutankhamun's tomb from 1352 BC is opened to reveal a 2,448 pound gold coffin and hundreds of gold objects. (I knew about that—the curse of the mummy—King Tut.)

Gold

AD 1511: King Ferdinand of Spain sends explorers to the New World to "get gold."

1500 BC: Gold-bearing regions of Nubia make Egypt a wealthy nation[8].

There were also some notes about goldsmiths in Peru in 1200 BC, and Sumerian royal tombs having gold objects. One thing is certain: gold has always been valuable even back to the days of the Sumerians—4000 BC. But why?

I kept surfing on the Internet. How about "What is gold," by Newmont Mining Corporation.

Hmm—properties of gold.

"Gold is the most non-reactive of all metals. Gold never reacts with oxygen. It will not rust or tarnish. The gold mask of Tutankhamun looked as brilliant when it was unearthed in AD 1922 as when it was buried in 1352 BC." (Well, that would make it valuable. Maybe I'm getting somewhere!)

"Gold is the most ductile of all metals, allowing it to be made into tiny threads without breaking." (Rumplestiltskin! The author of Rumplestiltskin must have known this because Rumplestiltskin was spinning straw into gold thread.)

"Gold is the most reflective and least absorptive material of infrared energy. Gold reflects up to 99 percent of infrared rays. This makes gold ideal for face shields for astronauts[9]." (So! That's why the astronauts used gold sun visors on the moon. Things like that fascinate me.)

All of these facts were interesting, but why would *everyone* want gold? Why was it used for money by so many civilizations? I had to admit, Old One, the old goat, had a great question. Why has gold been sought after more than diamonds or platinum or silver?

During the next few evenings I checked more Web sites, but didn't come across anything better than what I just told you. Out of desperation, I went to the souvenir shop in Babylon that sold books. I scanned the bookshelves, looking for information about gold. I can read (not speak) Arabic, one of the main languages in Iraq. To my surprise, I came across a book in English called *Genesis Revisited*. I picked it up because it was in English. As I looked through it, I came to a page about South African gold mining. There was something very curious on this page. When the South Africans were looking for places to dig for gold, they searched for abandoned mine sites. They found gold whenever they dug into the areas around the abandoned mine sites. These mine sites were very old. Charcoal and other items found in the abandoned mines were carbon dated to be at least forty thousand years old, maybe much older[10]! Who was digging for gold in South Africa forty thousand years ago? Cave men? Neanderthals? What would they use gold for? Nose rings for their wives? I decided this couldn't be true. Gold mining forty thousand years ago! Who wrote this book? Zecharia Sitchin. Hmm.

I began asking people at work what they knew about gold. No one knew anything! The metal that had caused the rise and fall of civilizations was pretty much a mystery. I was frustrated, and as you can probably tell, becoming obsessed with this. When I am frustrated and obsessed with something, I sometimes read the Bible. It takes my mind off my problems, like watching a soap opera. Lying on my small, uncomfortable military cot, I opened my Orthodox Bible. My Aunt Sophia is Russian Orthodox, and she gave this bible to me when I was ten years old. I brought it with me to Iraq. Book of *Genesis*. I skipped to Chapter 2.

It only took a minute and the words hit me: "And a river went out of Eden to water the garden; And from thence it was parted and became into four hands. The name of the first is Pison: That is it, which compasseth the whole land of Havilah, where there is gold; And the gold of that land is good: There is bdellium and the onyx stone." (*Genesis* 2:10-12)

There was gold in the Garden of Eden, and the gold was good! So, God cared about gold, and also bdellium, and the onyx stone. Bdellium is like myrrh. It is a fragrance or a perfume. Onyx is a gem that is transparent. God located Eden where gold, bdellium, and onyx stones were, especially *gold*. Gold that was good!

I have read Genesis and never really noticed that before. I felt dumb and smart at the same time. Now I have an answer for Old One: gold is the most valuable because it doesn't tarnish, it does things like reflect radiation, and God thinks it's important since it was in the Garden of Eden. Could that be the answer that Old One was looking for?

I ran around telling everyone about this, and curiously, no one seemed to care. Ricky thought I had heat stroke. It had been 114 degrees today in Iraq.

The next morning I found Scoot and asked him to take me to Old One. The giant Old One was working in the museum, re-cataloging items that had been recovered by the Marines nearby in the town of Saddamiat al-Tharthar.

I tripped as I walked into the museum. For a second, volleyball class at Penn State flashed across my brain. I always fell down and was afraid of the ball. I even twisted my ankle once.

I stumbled forward about three steps and caught myself on a display case.

Old One was just staring at me. I had to say something.

"Um, hello, sir." I didn't know his name, and calling him Old One seemed rude. "Do you remember me?"

He didn't answer my question. Instead he asked, "You have an answer?"

"Um, uh, yes, gold is the most valuable because it does not tarnish, it does things like reflect radiation, and because God thought it was valuable. In the book of *Genesis* in the Bible, it says God located the Garden of Eden where there was gold."

I stopped talking and waited nervously for a response. Old One seemed to be thinking deeply. Finally he made a pronouncement.

"That will do, Joy DiNardo. There is more with gold, but not now." He paused again. How did he know my name? "You are one of the people of the Book. Do you believe in the theory of evolution?"

The theory of evolution? Why would he ask me about that?

"Of course, yes, yes, um, I do."

Old One looked away from me. Then he said, while looking in the other direction, "Find why there is no missing link. You might use your Book."

The Missing Link

He turned and walked into another room, closing a door behind him. I stood there, surprised, alone, looking at the door. I started to feel angry. How could he have walked away, just like that, and left me standing there? Maybe that was how Iraqis acted; maybe it's a cultural thing. Then again, maybe it was just the way the old goat Old One acted. He was a very strange person. I left feeling kind of disappointed. Evolution, missing link, people of the Book. I ran into Scoot, and I told him the whole conversation. He just laughed. He thought Old One was crazy, and I was starting to agree with him.

Ricky and Lisa told me to forget about Old One. We had too much work to do, and I shouldn't waste time on this. On August 20, a delegation from the U.S. Senate and House of Representatives was coming to visit and we had to make sure that the communication and electrical facilities were working. I concentrated on my job and forgot about Old One for a few days.

After about a week, I ran into Scoot again. He had told my story to a Marine named Ma'ad, who is a Moslem. Ma'ad said that Moslems call Christians and Jews the "People of the Book." The "Book" is the Bible. So, I guess Old One is a Moslem, and when he said to use my "Book" to find out about evolution, he meant my Bible.

Once again, I couldn't resist working on Old One's question. What was in the Bible about evolution? I thought the Bible contradicted evolution. I explained this to Ricky and Lisa at dinner. Lisa again told me to forget about Old One.

"There's something really weird about that guy. You should just stay away from him."

Ricky tried to help me. He's Jewish, and so he had an English version of the Torah, the Jewish Bible, here in Iraq. It comprises the first five books of the Christian Bible.

Ricky's version was taken directly from the original Hebrew, which was closer to the original writings than my Aunt Sophia's Orthodox Bible. He told me to take care of it, because it had been given to him at his bar mitzvah.

That night, sitting on my uncomfortable military cot, I found some very interesting things in the Torah, in *Genesis*, the Creation Story. First of all, God was called Elohim in Ricky's Torah; Elohim created this and Elohim rested, and so on. Here is what was written in Ricky's Torah[12]:

On day three of creation, Elohim created plants. Elohim said:
"Let the Earth bring forth plants,
and grasses that yield seeds and fruit trees
that bear fruit of all kinds." (*Genesis* 1:11)

This was before there were any animals. God created plants first.

On day five of creation, Elohim said:
"Let the waters swarm with living creatures,
and let the aves fly above the earth…
and Elohim created Taninim,
and all the living creatures that crawl." (*Genesis* 1:20-21)

"Taninim" could mean sea serpents or crocodiles in Hebrew[11]. Anyway, next God created fish in the sea, birds, and living creatures that crawl.

On day six of creation, Elohim said:
"Let the Earth bring forth living animals
according to their kind:
bovines, and those that creep, and
beasts of the land." (*Genesis* 1:24-25)

Bovines are cows or cattle. I had to look that up. I had never heard anyone refer to cows as bovines. Hey Sam, go out and milk the bovines. Instead of cowboys, it's bovine-boys. Like, a rhinestone bovine-boy. (I always liked that song—Glen Campbell, "Rhinestone Cowboy").

OK—the Bible and Torah put everything in just about the same order as the anthropologists say evolution occurred. Plants, fish, birds and crawling creatures, bovines, and beasts of the land. And then, of course, the last to be created was us, people. The Bible is saying the same thing as the evolutionists.

Where the Bible got off track was with the story of Adam and Eve in the Garden of Eden. Everyone knows we descended from hominids. Well, let me rephrase that—a lot of people believe we descended from hominids. We just can't find the fossil record that shows the progression from ape-like creatures to human--"the missing link." How does Old One expect me to find it when all the anthropologists in the world can't? This is impossible.

I lay down on my uncomfortable military cot and drifted off to sleep. Fortunately, the brain continues to think while we sleep. Sometimes, it even solves our daytime problems. When I woke up in the morning, it hit me. Old One didn't say to find the missing link. He said there was no missing link! What could that mean, there is no missing link? How could there be no missing link?

As soon as I had a chance, I was back on the Internet—a new Web site that listed all the hominid species ever discovered. Here are the highlights: a partial list of our hominid ancestors, when they lived, and their brain sizes:

1. Australopithecus Anamensis 4.2 to 3.9 million years ago
                          Brain size: not listed
2. Australopithecus Afarensis 3.9 to 3.0 million years ago
                          Brain size: 375-550cc
3. Australopithecus Africans 3.0 to 2.0 million years ago
                          Brain size: 420-500cc
4. Homo Habilis   2.1 to 1.1 million years ago
                          Brain size: 500-800cc

Homo Habilis was also known as "handy man," not because of the way he behaved on dates, but because they found primitive tools with his remains.

5. Homo Erectus   1.8 million to 300,000 years ago
                          Brain size: 750-1225cc

This guy used primitive tools and maybe fire.

6. Homo Sapiens   500,000 to 200,000 years ago

"There is no clear dividing line between Homo erectus and Homo sapiens." I looked on a Homo erectus Web site. It said that some Homo erectus remains were found on Java, and dated to only forty thousand years ago. So, they didn't evolve into Homo sapiens.

7. Homo Neanderthalis   230,000 to 30,000 years ago
                               Brain size: 1450cc

This was Neanderthal Man. He was the first to bury the dead. He also had tools and weapons, and he could speak!

8. Homo Sapiens Sapiens   195,000 years ago to present
                               Brain size: 1350cc

We are Homo sapiens sapiens.

Homo sapiens sapiens developed artwork and musical instruments. Homo sapiens sapiens could speak. I wonder if they talked to Neanderthals?

Then the Web site said about forty thousand years ago, with the appearance of the Cro-Magnon culture, tool kits started becoming more sophisticated. The Cro-Magnon culture existed in Southern Europe and the Middle East. They had tool kits and cave art[13]. ·

I sat there and looked at the schedule. It seemed like not much happened for millions of years and then BOOM! Neanderthals started burying their dead, made weapons and tools, and could speak. Homo sapiens sapiens made artwork, tool kits, musical instruments, and could speak. Something happened around two hundred thousand years ago. I also noticed that the Cro-Magnon culture developed forty thousand years ago, the same time as the South African gold mines. You don't think *Genesis Revisited* was correct? No, it's not possible. Anyway, it seemed the answer to the missing link problem could be found around two hundred thousand years ago.

I decided to go back to the Babylon bookstore. As I looked on the shelves, I was drawn again to *Genesis Revisited* by Zecharia Sitchin[14]. The book was like a magnet. On the cover, it has a brightly colored drawing of the Garden of Eden—very enticing. I paged through the book again. One chapter was titled "The Mother Called Eve." I began reading. A conference was held at Cambridge University in 1987 to update new findings about "The Origins and Dispersal of Modern Man." What they reported is complicated. I had to read this a few times, so bear with me.

In the late 1980s, it was discovered that only women have something called Mitochondrial DNA in their cells. We're special. The special DNA passes from grandmother to mother to daughter and on forever without changing, so you can trace the ancestry of a woman back to the beginning of time. Someone from Emory University did this for eight hundred women of different races. He found that their Mitochondrial DNA was so similar that they all descended from a single female ancestor. The same thing was done at the University of Michigan, University of California at Berkeley, and University of Hawaii. They all reached the conclusion that those tested had a common female ancestor who lived between 300,000 and 150,000 years ago! In fact, everyone had this same female ancestor.

That ancestor had to be Eve. I was right. Something *did* happen two hundred thousand years ago—Eve.

Back on my uncomfortable military cot, I read from another source on the Internet that testing of Nuclear DNA might prove Eve's descendants interbred with hominids in certain areas instead of replacing them. I didn't want to confuse the issue, so I put that in the back of my cranium.

Where did Eve come from? That was the question I had to answer. Old One said I might use my Book. OK, I went back to Ricky's Torah, the Creation of Man, *Genesis* 1:26: "Elohim said, 'Let us make an Adam in our image and after our likeness." Wait a minute. Who was "*us*?" Who was "*our*?" It said "Let *us* make an Adam in *our* image…" Was that a misprint in Ricky's English version of the Torah[15]?

I decided to look in my trusty Orthodox Bible.

"God said, let us make man in our image and likeness." (*Genesis* 1:26) There it was again. God made man, and He had help. Who helped God to make man? Who was "*us*?" Who was "*our*?"

Something else was weird. My Bible said God created man and woman at the same time, and then put man only into the Garden of Eden to work. "And God created man to his own image: to the image of God he created him. Male and female he created them. And God blessed them…And the Lord God took man, and put him into the paradise of pleasure, to dress it, and to keep it." (*Genesis* 1:27-28, 2:15)

That's not what I was taught in Sunday school.

Now I'm confused about Adam and Eve, but at least I think I have the answer for Old One. There is no missing link because hominids did not evolve into Homo sapiens sapiens—us. We were created by God, who had help from someone else around two hundred thousand years ago.

The Bible tells the whole story of evolution in order: plants, fish, birds, animals that crawl, beasts of the land, and then God and someone else

15

created man and woman, putting man only into the Garden of Eden to work, and there was gold in Eden.

The evidence from the fossil record and Mitochondrial DNA seemed to prove what the Bible says. Old One was right when he said to use my book—my Bible.

The Nephilim

The delegation from Congress came and went. They toured Saddam's palace, some of the ruins of Babylon, and looked around the museum. Then a couple of them made speeches about what a great job we were doing and how much they supported us. They posed and smiled for the cameras, and then they left as quickly as they came. That seemed to be what they cared about the most—being in front of the cameras. I was glad when they were gone so we could relax.

I was also anxious to see Old One. I found him again in the museum where he seemed to be doing something with piece of a broken clay tablet. He looked at me, and his large eyes brightened a little. I smiled.

"Hello. Do you remember me? I think that I have the answer to your new question."

Old One half smiled and said, "Ayyamkum Saeeda." (That is a traditional Iraqi greeting. It means, "May your days be happy.")

I nodded my head. "Thank you. I have the answer to your question. Um, there is no missing link because hominids did not evolve into humans. We were created by God about two hundred thousand years ago. Also, God did not do this alone. He is quoted in my book as saying let *us* make man in *our* image." I stopped talking. Old One was quiet for a minute. He seemed to be lost in thought.

"When you discover the truth you must accept it, Joy DiNardo." He had a sad look in his very large eyes as he spoke. I wondered why he said that. Did I sound like I didn't believe what I had told him? That made me worry. If he thinks I'm not serious, he may decide I'm not worthy of learning the truth anymore.

"Sir, I believe what I just said. The theory of evolution is true except for our part. Humans are the exception. *There is no missing link!*"

Old One didn't continue the conversation, saying only "When you see me again, you may tell me who the Nephilim are. I must work now." He turned around and began fiddling with the broken piece of clay tablet.

Did he say *Nephilim*? I turned and walked toward the door. Then I stopped. *Nephilim*? I wanted to ask him to repeat that but didn't. I started walking out of the door. *Nephilim*! Reminds me of Winnie-the-Pooh! *Nephilim*, and Tigger and Roo. I went back to work. *Nephilim*! I have to remember that word.

The next day, all nonmilitary personnel were called to a meeting with the base commander, Lt. Ortiz. We were told that the situation in Iraq had become more unsettled. Terrorists from Syria, Iran, Jordan, and Saudi Arabia were entering Iraq and joining with the Iraqis still loyal to Saddam Hussein. Their method of fighting was unconventional. They were using terrorist tactics: suicide bombings, kidnapping, and roadside bombs. They would not hesitate to kill civilians. Some Halliburton employees had already been killed near Mosul. Therefore, security was being tightened on the base. We were not supposed to go outside of a triangular work area, making me feel like a prisoner. The information about Halliburton employees being killed made me feel a little shaken. I hadn't really considered that I was in a life-threatening situation. I decided not to think about it. There wasn't much I could do about it anyway.

At dinner, Ricky and Lisa wanted to talk about the meeting with Lt. Ortiz. I wanted to ask Ricky about Nephilim. I listened for awhile, but as soon as I had a chance, I changed the subject.

"Did you guys ever hear of Nephilim?"

They both stared at me. Lisa finished chewing her food before asking "What did you say?"

I felt a little embarrassed, but I repeated the question. "Nephilim. Did you ever hear of Nephilim?"

"Uh, sounds like some kind of fabric, like nylon?" Lisa started eating again.

Ricky had been staring at me. He took a sip from his milk carton, and then said "I know what they are."

"They?" Lisa didn't glance up from her food to ask.

"Yes. They're in the Torah and the Bible, in *Genesis*."

Lisa pointed her fork at me. "Is this another 'Old One' thing?" She began lecturing me about wasting my time with this strange Iraqi that we know nothing about. Our lives are in danger, and I'm playing games like this. Her fork was twirling in the air. I tried to defend myself.

"But Lisa, I've learned a lot of things."

Lisa frowned at me. Her eyes narrowed, and she leaned forward, pointing her fork at me again.

I kept talking. "Like, it says in the Bible that God didn't create us by Himself. God said let *us* create man in *our* image. Also, He created man and woman together somewhere, and then put man only into the Garden of Eden."

Lisa was still pointing her fork at me. "Joy, do you think that these things are direct quotes from God? Did 'Old One' tell you that?"

"Well, not exactly," I responded meekly.

Lisa's fork was moving back and forth in front of my face. "That doesn't mean anything because it says *us* instead of *me*. Maybe *us* was the Trinity, you know, three beings in one God."

"But Lisa, the Hebrews wrote *Genesis*. They didn't know about the Trinity idea."

Lisa made a face at me, and shook her head. "It still doesn't mean anything."

Ricky was strangely quiet and seemed uncomfortable. Having grown up in an Orthodox Jewish family, he had studied the Torah for many years. I wondered why he was so nervous, but didn't say anything.

That night, sitting on my uncomfortable military cot, I opened Ricky's English version of the Torah again to look for Nephilim in *Genesis*. I came to Chapter 5, *The Descendants of Adam*. It didn't mention Nephilim, but it said something surprising: "This is the book of the generations of Adam. In the day that God created man he made him to the likeness of God. He created them, male and female, and called their name Adam in the day when they were created." (*Genesis* 5:1-2)

Here again God created man and woman *together*, and named them *both* Adam. So this is different from the story that Eve was created from Adam's rib! The story of Adam's rib has been used through the ages to prove men were superior to women. But here, in the same book, it also says we were created *together*. This is different from whatever happened in the Garden of Eden, and men and women are equal because God called us *both* Adam. I wonder what Adam means. Why Adam? I wished that Lisa had been there so that I could've shown this to her. I kept reading. In Chapter 6, *Genesis*, I found the Nephilim. This was a very strange passage:

And it came to pass, when men began to multiply on the face of
the earth, and daughters were born unto them, that the sons of
God saw the daughters of men that they were fair; and they took
them wives of all which they chose…

…There were *Nephilim* on the earth in those days; and also after
that, when the sons of God came in unto the daughters of men,
and they bare children to them, the same became mighty men
which were of old, men of renown[15].

I read the same passage in my Bible, but it used the word "giants" instead of Nephilim.

A footnote at the bottom of the page claimed that people were of larger stature before the flood (Noah's Flood) than after the flood. It didn't
explain why.

None of this made sense to me. I had to do more research. By now,
we had Internet hookups everywhere. I was able to use my laptop computer here on my uncomfortable military cot. I typed in "Nephilim." On
another Web site, I found that the word Nephilim is a Hebrew word
meaning "those who came down," or "those who descended[16]." Came
down from where?

Another of the Nephilim Web sites was linked to the *Antiquities of the
Jews*, a historical document written in the first century AD by Flavius
Josephus. I've heard of him. He was a Roman/Jewish historian. Here was
his explanation of the Nephilim, and it made things more confusing:
"Many angels of God accompanied with women, and begat sons that became unjust…on account of the confidence they had in their own
strength; for the tradition is that these men did what resembled the acts of
those whom the Grecians call giants[17]."

Angels? Grecians? Now bear with me. I know this is getting tedious.
There was another Web site I went to which told about a lost text called
The Book of the Wars of Yahweh. Some of this text is contained in the Bibli-
cal books of *Numbers* and *Deuteronomy*[18].

According to *Numbers,* Yahweh was the God of the Israelites. He had
led the Israelites out of Egypt and into the Sinai Desert where they stayed
to prepare to enter the Promised Land. The Promised Land was the land
of Canaan, which is now Israel and parts of the surrounding countries.
Canaan was occupied by other people. Some were giants, and Yahweh
commanded the Israelites to conquer them.

Before the Israelites attacked Canaan, they sent twelve spies into the land. It was harvest time and they saw grapes and other fruits that were larger than normal—large enough for giants to eat. Furthermore, the people of Canaan were larger than the Israelites. The spies reported that the land was filled with giants. Only two of the twelve spies, Joshua and Caleb, believed they could defeat these giants.

Joshua led the Israelites into battle. With Yahweh's help, they conquered the giants, such as the giant King Og of Bashan. The *Book of Deuteronomy* describes his bed as made of iron and eighteen feet long! They defeated the Raphaims, Emims, Anakims, and other giant tribes[19].

The Israelites eventually defeated Goliath who was reported to be thirteen feet, six inches tall, and the Giant of Gath who had twelve fingers and twelve toes. To conquer the Promised Land, the Israelites had to defeat the Nephilim[20].

OK, what have I learned today? My dad always told me that I should learn something new every day.

1. God had sons who married women—human women.

2. Flavius Josephus called them angels instead of God's sons. (I'm not sure if I believe in angels.) So, God's sons or angels married human women and their children were giants, like Og, Goliath, and others.

3. The word Nephilim doesn't mean "giant," like my Bible says, it means "those who came down." But, the Nephilim were giants, so my Bible wasn't incorrect. "Those who came down" probably refers to God's sons or the angels who had to come down to earth to marry human women. It also refers to their offspring.

4. The Nephilim lived in the land of Canaan, which today is Israel and some of the surrounding countries.

5. Yahweh, the God of the Israelites, commanded them to conquer the Nephilim.

This all seemed pretty unbelievable to me. However, this was in the Bible, the Torah, the *Antiquities of the Jews*, and *The Book of the Wars of Yahweh*. Then the words of Old One made their way into my brain: *When you discover the truth, you must accept it, Joy DiNardo.*

OK, I was ready to talk to Old One again. I was so wound up that I lay on my uncomfortable military cot most of the night with my eyes open, thinking.

Luckily, the museum was in the triangular area I could enter without an escort. The next morning, that is where I found Old One.

21

"Um, hello again. I found out about the Nephilim."

Old One was sitting in a chair. Raising his eyes to meet mine, he waited.

"Sons of God or angels married human women and produced offspring who were giants. These giants were called Nephilim in the Torah." Old One seemed to make a face. Maybe I had the wrong answer. Panic began to set in. I kept going. "The Nephilim lived in the land of Canaan. Yahweh commanded the Israelites to conquer Canaan. So they did. The Israelites' leader was named Joshua. The Bible names some Nephilim. Og, King of Bashan, had a bed that was eighteen feet long. Goliath was thirteen feet, six inches tall." I hesitated for a moment as it hit me that Old One was extremely tall. "The Nephilim were wiped out by the Israelites."

I stopped talking. There was another one of those awkward silences.

Finally, he spoke. "Do you understand why I said that you *may* tell me about the Nephilim?"

"Um, yes. I think so. I guess I have the wrong information."

I had failed.

"It is not exactly wrong," Old One said. "It is not exactly right. Perhaps you need a change in direction. Tell me, what is the real name of your Jesus? Tell me where He was after He left the temple."

"OK, thank you." I turned and walked out of the museum. I can't believe I just said *OK, thank you*. I must have seemed like a real moron. How embarrassing!

A feeling of inadequacy came over me. I'm still not sure who or what the Nephilim and the sons of God are.

The Real Name of Jesus and the Temple

The next month, several unexpected things happened to me. Before I get to those, I need to summarize everything I've learned so far:

1. God located the Garden of Eden where there was gold. That is why gold has always been considered valuable, along with the fact that it doesn't tarnish and reflects radiation.

2. The Bible and the Torah tell the whole story of evolution.

3. Hominids did not evolve into humans. Humans were created separately, about two hundred thousand years ago.

4. God and someone else created man and woman together. This was done somewhere outside of the Garden of Eden.

5. God called both man and woman Adam. We are equal in God's eyes.

6. God put man only into the Garden of Eden to work.

7. God had sons who married human women.

8. God's sons and the human women had offspring that were giants. They were called Nephilim, which means "those who came down" in Hebrew.

9. The Nephilim were wiped out by the Israelites at the command of their God, Yahweh.

That was fairly different from what I had learned in Sunday school. A little thought entered my cerebral cortex. Those sons of God who came down to earth are extraterrestrial, right? I decided not to think about that anymore.

I wanted to do a good job on the real name of Jesus—better than I did with the Nephilim. I decided to e-mail Becky, my old college roommate.

Actually, she's not old. She's twenty-eight and also a trivia nerd.

She has a "Trivia Nerd" T-shirt too. She even applied to be a contestant on Jeopardy once.

Becky, Jesus Christ is not the real name of Jesus Christ. I know, that sounds stupid. Get as many sources as you can, and find out His real name.

I had confidence in Becky.

One evening, Lt. Sandal, Lt. Ortiz's assistant, walked into my sleeping quarters. He had an official letter from the Green Zone in Baghdad. I had to be ready to go to Camp Tallil in two hours. From there, I was going to Afghanistan on a temporary assignment for three weeks. The mission was classified, and that was all he could tell me.

The trip was grueling. I won't bore you with the details but I eventually found myself in a mountain pass in Northern Afghanistan. The closest city was Mazar-e-Sharif. My job was to work on an oil pipeline being built to connect to the Caspian Sea. I did other work too that is classified—I can't talk about it, which is very difficult for me. My living quarters were set up in an abandoned Buddhist monastery. The people here were mainly Afghan descendants of Uzbeks and Mongols, practicing Buddhism and Hinduism, not Islam. They liked Americans because we had overthrown the Taliban rulers of Afghanistan, who had treated them badly. The rulers had blown up two ancient and famous statues of Buddha carved into a solid rock cliff. Mullah Omar, the Taliban leader, had ordered all statues destroyed, ruling that all human likenesses of divinity are un-Islamic. The only God is Allah, and all other false gods should be removed[21].

Also, all women, regardless of their religion, were forced to cover themselves from head to toe when in public. If they didn't, men were allowed to beat them with sticks. That was the law of the Taliban. It's also the Adam's rib thing!

Still today, women wear headscarves and make sure that even their ankles are covered when they are out of the house. I wore a headscarf too. I was traveling with American Special Forces, but we still had to be careful in remote places.

An Indian woman from Kabul, the capital of Afghanistan, was also with us. She was an electrical engineer, and her name was Mena. She had beautiful, long, black hair, but had to keep it covered. I found her to be very friendly and pleasant. If we had more time, we could have become good friends.

Every evening we were exhausted and went right to sleep. One evening, though, I decided to read my trusty Orthodox Bible. I wanted to find out where Jesus went after He left the temple. I remember the story. Jesus came to Jerusalem with His parents, Mary and Joseph, when He was about twelve years old. He wandered off, and His parents couldn't find Him for three days. They finally located Him in the temple, debating with the Hebrew priests and teachers. Mary scolded Him, asking Jesus how He could do such a thing that caused great worry to her and Joseph. Jesus answered: "Do you not know that I have to be about my Father's business?" Jesus, at the age of twelve, knew that his Father was God, not Joseph. So, where did He go after the temple?

There are four books in the New Testament of the Bible that tell about Jesus' life: *Matthew, Mark, Luke,* and *John.* It had to be in one of those. I scanned all four books.

In *Matthew,* Jesus was born in Bethlehem and taken to Egypt with his parents when He was a baby to escape King Herod. He came back after Herod died. The story then jumps to when He was thirty years old and baptized by John the Baptist in the Jordan River, skipping His teens and twenties.

Mark starts with the baptism in the Jordan River when Jesus was thirty years old.

Luke tells the story of Jesus in the temple. After His parents found Him, they took Him back to their home. Then it also jumps to the baptism in the Jordan River at age thirty.

John starts with a poem about God and the beginning of the world, then jumps to the baptism when Jesus was thirty years old.

It wasn't in the Bible. That's amazing! It's like Jesus disappeared for those years. In Bible school, the teachers said Jesus spent His teen years and His twenty-something years working as a carpenter with Joseph. But how do they know that? It doesn't say anything about it in the Bible.

Mena asked me what I was reading. I didn't feel like talking so I said very softly "the Bible," trying to act as if I was deeply engrossed in it and should not be disturbed. Of course, that didn't work.

Mena replied, "The Old Testament or the New Testament?" That surprised me. I figured that she was a Hindu. How did she know that?

"New Testament."

"About St. Issa?" Mena asked.

I didn't quite make out what she had said, because the name wasn't familiar to me, and Mena spoke with an Indian accent.

"Pardon me?" I asked.

Mena repeated the question. "You are reading about St. Issa?"

St. Issa? I wondered who that was. "No, Mena. It's about Jesus Christ."

Mena kind of nodded her head. Her eyes brightened. "Jesus Christ is St. Issa." She sounded happy for some reason. I wanted to just say OK, whatever, but I'm one of those people who have guilt trips if I'm rude. I tried to explain this.

"Mena, Jesus Christ is not St. Issa. Jesus Christ was from Israel. We believe that He is the Son of God."

I thought that was a reasonable explanation. Mena laughed. Why was she laughing? She began to laugh harder.

"What's so funny?" I laughed too, because Mena was laughing.

I hadn't laughed in awhile, and it felt good. I realized I had no idea why I was laughing. I stopped. I probably came across once again as being an idiot. Mena became serious too.

"Joy, in Kabul there is an ancient pond. It was there two thousand years ago. Your Jesus bathed in it. That is why today it is called the Pond of Issa[22]."

Now I had heard everything! Jesus bathed in a pond in Afghanistan, and the people there called Him St. Issa. Then something seeped into the outer areas of my brain. Old One. He had said I needed a change of direction. Afghanistan was a change of direction! He also said when I find the truth, I should accept it. This was getting creepy. I decided to torture myself some more.

"Mena, tell me what you know about St. Issa, Jesus."

Mena smiled. "It is a curious thing that most Christians do not know this. Whenever they discover it, they refuse to think about it. Many in Kabul and India know that your Jesus was here. I will tell you."

Mena's voice was soft and pleasant—good for telling stories. "The age of thirteen was when Israelite men took a wife," she began. "When Issa became thirteen, His house began to be a place of meeting for rich and noble people who desired to have Issa as a son-in-law. He was already famous for his wisdom and discourses about God."

"Issa did not want to marry. He wanted to obtain enlightenment and perfection through devotional service to God. When Issa found out that His father, Joseph, had accepted a marriage proposal for Him, He secretly left Israel with a trade caravan."

"The trade caravan went to the land of Sind. (I found out later that Sind was in Southern Pakistan.) While traveling, He was immediately recognized by the Jains as one who had received the mercy of the Lord. Joy, do you know what Jains are?"

I didn't know, but I said yes anyway. I think they're like Hindus.

Mena continued. "Issa went to the city of Juggernaut (Juggernaut is on the coast of India), where the white priests of Brahma made Him a joyous welcome. They taught Issa to read and understand the Vedas, which are Hindu scriptures, to cure by aid of prayer, to teach, and to drive out evil spirits from people so as to restore them to their sanity. Issa was beloved by everyone. He even lived in peace with the Vaisyas and the Sudras. (These are the lower caste Hindus. The Sudras were used as slaves by the Brahmans.) Issa preached the Vedas to them, which was forbidden, and tried to lift their position in society."

Mena's voice was so relaxing that my eyes started to get heavy. Suddenly, my Bible fell out of my hand and onto my foot.

"OW."

Mena laughed. Why am I always clumsy?

Mena began again. "The Brahmans wanted to kill Issa for what He was doing, and so He left Juggernaut. He had been there for six years. Issa went to Gautamides, the birthplace of the great Buddha in the Himalayan Mountains. He studied the sacred Sutras. Sutras are the Buddhist scriptures.

"After six years in the Himalayan Mountains, Issa left and traveled westward towards Israel. He preached to all the different peoples that He met along the way. In Persia, which is Iran today, the priests became alarmed and forbade the inhabitants to listen to Him. They arrested Issa and interrogated Him, and then they let Him go.

"Issa had reached His twenty-ninth year when He returned to the land of Israel[22]."

That was quite a story. I didn't know whether to believe it. I thought about Mena and St. Issa a lot on the trip back to Babylon the next week. I wished I had been able to spend more time with Mena.

On October 16, a ceremony was held on the base for Lt. Ortiz, the base commander, who had been killed by a roadside bomb as he was traveling through the nearby province of Karbala. His assistant, Lt. Sandal, had also been killed.

A bugler began to play taps. Taps is such a solemn, penetrating song.

While he played, there wasn't another sound on the whole base. Some of the soldiers had tears in their eyes. Their commander was dead. I started to think of my own mortality. Did I really have a soul? Is there really a heaven? Is there life after death?

I was feeling down when I returned to my uncomfortable military cot. To distract myself, I logged onto my laptop and found an e-mail from Becky about Jesus' name. She listed twelve sources. Good old Becky. She probably had her "Trivia Nerd" T-shirt on while she sent the e-mail. She listed the *SDA Bible Dictionary*, Ian Wilson's *Jesus, the Evidence*, *The Anchor Bible*, and on and on.

First of all, there was no "J" in ancient Hebrew, ruling out Jesus as His actual name. Christ comes from the Greek work *Christos*, which means "anointed." Most of the twelve sources said that the real name of Jesus was Yahoshu, but because of the different dialects used in Israel, it was pronounced either Yoshua or Yeshua. That is what they believed Mary called Him[23].

I like that better than Jesus. Yeshua. The name Yahoshu comes from *Yaho*, the poetic form of Yahweh and *shu*, which means "save." Yahweh saves! So Jesus' real name was Yahoshu, and it meant "Yahweh saves[24]."

Then Becky proved to me she is still a genius like she was in college. At the end of all of the references, she cited an Arabic book, *Tariq-A-Ajhan*, which says that a fair is held in Kabul, Afghanistan every year to mark a special event. Near Kabul, there is a wayside pond where Jesus rested and washed His hands and feet. The pond still exists and is known as Issa-pond, because Jesus' name in that part of the world is St. Issa! The fair commemorates that event.

I sent an e-mail to Becky.

Becky, you are still a genius. Is there anything else you can find out about St. Issa?

A few days later, Becky wrote back to me. She only found two sources that talked about St. Issa. One was an entire book called *The Lost Years of Jesus* by Elizabeth Clare Prophet. First, the book tells the story of Jesus in India and the East, the same as Mena explained it. Then, it explained the discovery of scrolls at a monastery at Hemis, a village in the Himalayan Mountains that told the story of Issa. Evidently, in 1887, a Russian journalist named Nicolas Notovich was traveling in that area and had fallen from a horse and broken his leg. He was taken to the monastery for medical treatment, where the chief Lama read to him the story of Issa. The Lama said he had many scrolls that described the life and acts of

Buddha Issa, who preached in India and Israel! Notovich published his findings in two papers called "The Life of St. Issa" and "The Unknown Life of Christ." Shortly after that, another journalist named J. Archibald Douglas visited the monastery at Hemis. The monks told him they knew nothing of St. Issa, so Notovich was criticized and called a fraud by everyone, including the *New York Times*.

Then in 1921, a tourist named Henrietta Merrick visited the monastery and was told the same thing as Notovich. In 1922, a Hindu scholar, Swami Abhedananda, visited the monastery and saw the scrolls. He was also shown another copy of the same scrolls at a monastery in Lhasa, Tibet[25].

In 1928, a professor, Nickolai Roerich, traveling through India, visited the monastery at Hemis and found the scrolls concerning St. Issa, which were kept in the most isolated part of underground storage areas.

In 1939, a tourist named Elisabeth Caspari was shown three books by the librarian at Hemis. He exclaimed, "These books say your Jesus was here!"

The story kind of died until the 1970s. Then Dr. Robert Ravicz, a cultural anthropologist, was told about the Issa manuscripts when he was at Hemis. About the same time, a traveler named Edward Noack was told by another monk at Hemis that the manuscripts existed. After that, the story ends again. The area has been taken over by communist China, which tries to suppress Buddhism, and so contact with lamas and monks is restricted. According to Becky, all of that information was in the book *The Lost Years of Jesus*. I'm going to buy that book when I get home.

That reminded me of what Mena had said about Jesus studying Buddhism. William Bramley wrote in his book, *The Gods of Eden,* that Jesus' "Sermon on the Mount" contains philosophy strikingly similar to the Buddhism of His day.

Becky sent all of that in one e-mail. I missed good old Becky. She's not really old. Becky is tall, has blond hair and blue eyes, and is extremely smart. She also wasn't afraid of the ball in volleyball class. Becky works for NASA at the Kennedy Space Center, is married, and has a beautiful little daughter. I hated Becky!

The "Sermon on the Mount" is my favorite teaching of Jesus, Yeshua. For some reason, only Luke records it in his gospel (not Matthew, Mark, or John). I had to write some of it because it was in my brain, and I can't keep things in there:

"Blessed are the poor in spirit (that means humble), for theirs is the Kingdom of Heaven."

"Blessed are the meek, for they shall inherit the earth."

"Blessed are the peacemakers, for they--"

Wait a minute! Wait one minute!

This was cause and effect. If you do something good, then something good will happen to you. If you were poor in spirit, meaning humble, then yours is the Kingdom of Heaven. If you do something bad, something bad will happen to you. Jesus said "Woe to you who are filled (that means greedy) for you shall hunger." Cause and effect. *That is the Buddhist law of Karma.* The "Sermon on the Mount" was teaching about Karma! I have a book called *Buddhism for Beginners* by Thubten Chodren[26]. I brought it here to Iraq. I dug the book out from my luggage and turned to page fifty-nine, "What is Karma?" "If chili seeds are planted, chili will grow, not apples. In the same way if we act constructively, happiness will ensue; if we act destructively, problems will result." That is what Yeshua was teaching in the "Sermon on the Mount": Karma. William Bramley was right[27].

A couple days later, Becky sent more information to me. Nicolas Notovich claimed that the Roman Catholic Church has copies of sixty-three of these scrolls about St. Issa, and was suppressing this information. I can't understand why. This information made the story of Jesus seem even more wonderful.

I decided that I would share this with Lisa and Ricky. At dinner one evening, I told them I had discovered something surprising when I was in Afghanistan. It was confirmed by my friend Becky, who works for NASA and is a genius.

"*Jesus Christ spent half of His life in India!*"

Lisa laughed so hard I thought her head was going to roll off. Her shoulders heaved up and down and she looked like a volcano erupting. Ricky just smiled and had a look on his face like he felt sorry for me, dismissing the whole idea. Mena had said that most Christians, whenever they discover this, refuse to think about it. That explains Lisa's reaction, but Ricky is Jewish. Maybe it was all in the delivery?

The next day I went to see Old One. I told him that the answer to his question found me, I didn't find it. Jesus had been to India, Tibet, and other countries east of Israel after He left the temple. Also, His real name is Yahoshu, and it means Yahweh saves.

Old One nodded in approval. I felt pretty good.

Yahweh and Allah I

Old One did not talk anymore about Yeshua or India. He went right to a new topic. "Next you should find out who Yahweh and Allah are, and why they are carrying on a battle."

That didn't make any sense to me. "But Yahweh and Allah are the same person—God. There is only one God," I protested.

Old One seemed to be looking at my hair. "Joy DiNardo, just as there are many colors in your hair, there are many gods," he replied.

What did he say? My hair? He had said something about my hair! Remember when I said that I had strawberry blond hair and it's not my natural color? Well, I hadn't been able to dye my hair here. My brown roots had grown in. Also, the sun had bleached my hair in certain spots. So, my hair looked like Joseph's coat of many colors from the Bible. All I could say was "OK, fine."

I stormed out. Old One looked a little nervous for once. Never tell a woman there is something wrong with her appearance, even after five months in the desert!

I went straight to the power station where I worked and pouted. We are trying to provide power to Karbala, particularly to a school that the 101st Airborne was building. That's what Lt. Ortiz was doing in Karbala when he was killed by a roadside bomb—supervising the delivery of materials for the school construction.

I didn't begin working on Old One's new question right away. First, I had my hair cut by a Polish soldier who was also a beautician. The force here in Babylon is multi-national. My hair was cut to the bottom of my ears, so at least it was now all my natural color. I don't like myself with short hair.

The Polish soldier asked me what I did in my spare time. He probably wanted a date, but changed his mind when my answer was "read the Bible." He said he liked the *Books of Kings* in the Bible. The next time I opened my Bible I went right to the *Books of Kings* to see what they were about. I skipped around and ended up on Chapter 20. It talked about a tribe of people called the Arameans, who were defeated in battle when they attempted to invade Israel. Their generals said that to win, they would need to draw the Israelites out of their mountain strongholds and fight them on the plains because the Israelite God was a God of mountains, which was why the Israelites always prevailed. They were talking about Yahweh, the Israelite God—the God of the Bible. Yahweh was a God of the mountains, but not a God of the plains? Very interesting! I noticed that in the *Books of Kings* God was called Yahweh. In *Genesis*, in the Torah, God was referred to as Elohim. How did this Yahweh stuff get started? I looked through the Torah. There was *Deuteronomy, Numbers, Exodus,* and then *Genesis.* Yahweh began in *Exodus,* when God spoke to Moses. Here is what He said in Ricky's Torah: "I am who am. And I appeared unto Abraham, unto Isaac, and unto Jacob as El Shaddai; but by my name 'I am who am' I was not known to them." (*Exodus* 6:2-3)

I looked at the same passage in my Bible. According to a footnote, Yahweh is the Hebrew word for "I am who am." It kind of reminded me of Popeye. *I am what I am and that's all that I am—I'm Popeye the Sailor Man.* I take that back! I shouldn't compare Yahweh to Popeye.

Anyway, that was the first use of the name Yahweh.

But what was "El Shaddai"? I had to look that one up. Pulling out my laptop, I typed in "El Shaddai" and found a Web site by R. Aubuchon, Jr[28]. According to R. Aubuchon, Jr., *Shaddai* means "mountains" and *El* means "God." So *El Shaddai* meant "God of the mountains." The Arameans were right. Yahweh was a God of the mountains. Yahweh called Himself El Shaddai to Abraham, Isaac, and Jacob.

Something else was strange. In Hebrew, *El* means "one God" and *Elohim* means "many gods." Remember when I was reading the creation story in Ricky's Torah? The Torah said "Elohim" created man and woman. That means many gods created man and woman. Old One said there were many gods, just like my hair was many colors. But I changed it to one color. In *Exodus,* the Israelites changed from many gods (Elohim) to one God (Yahweh). This means the Israelites were not monotheistic. The term "monotheistic" means belief in only one God. Christians, Jews, and Moslems are monotheistic. They believe in one God. The Israelites were monolatory. The term "monolatory" means exclusive worship of only one god out of many gods. In ancient times, there were many gods, but the Israelites only worshipped one of them—Yahweh. Out of all the gods, the Israelites picked Yahweh to worship, or maybe Yahweh picked them. They are called the chosen people, chosen by Yahweh, the God of the mountains. But who were the other gods—the "Elohim?"

I would always do this to myself. It was midnight and I was awake on my uncomfortable military cot, trying to find out who the Elohim were. Could they be the "us" who created humans? I decided it was too confusing to think about at midnight, and went to sleep.

The next evening, I sat outside of the sleeping quarters with Ricky, talking about Thanksgiving. Next Thursday was Thanksgiving and I was looking forward to a good, turkey dinner. There was going to be a special service on the base. Everyone was invited. Thanksgiving in Babylon! Of course, I couldn't just sit there and talk about Thanksgiving all night. I asked Ricky about Yahweh and the Elohim.

Ricky's reaction was unexpected, to say the least. He looked at me and studied my facial expression for a moment. He seemed to be a little fearful. Then he began to speak. "A few years ago, a professor in Tel Aviv (Tel Aviv used to be the capital of Israel) created an uproar in the whole country of Israel. Among many wild claims, the professor said he had found Hebrew texts from around 800 BC mentioning the goddess Asherah as Yahweh's consort[29]."

I was surprised. "By consort, do you mean…" I paused, afraid to say the word, "like, um, girlfriend, wife?"

"Yes. Exactly." Ricky stood up. He paced back and forth like he was in deep thought, then sat down again, seeming to be very disturbed about this. "Joy, according to the professor, the Israelites also worshipped Asherah, Yahweh's wife. They did not adopt monotheism, belief in one God, until the sixth century BC, during the Babylonian captivity."

"Then they became monolatory," I interrupted.

Ricky nodded and took his glasses off. "Very good, Joy. They worshipped only one of many gods. According to the professor, they still believed many gods existed, but only worshipped one God. You see, religion can be so confusing. That is why I'm not Orthodox anymore."

Ricky looked down at the ground. I didn't know what to say. I didn't like the silence, so I began again. "And what happened to the professor?"

Ricky sighed. "The professor said other things that disputed the traditional story of the Israelites, and so he was condemned in both Israel and America. But archaeological records, ancient statues, and texts support his claim about Asherah. They discovered inscriptions near Hebron that refer to Yahweh and Asherah. Also, in Tenach, an Israelite settlement, they found cult stands that display a naked goddess between two lions, which is the symbol of Asherah. In Judah, they have found many little clay figures of a female that could be images of Asherah."

Ricky shook his head, and then asked one of those questions that doesn't have an answer. "How could God have a girlfriend?"

Well, that opened up a whole new can of worms. Yahweh, the God of the Bible, was also the God of the mountains, and He had a consort, the goddess Asherah! I left Ricky sitting there by himself. I really did! I just got up and left because I had to find out about Asherah.

I tried to find something in the Bible about Asherah. In the *Book of Kings III,* Chapter 11:5, it talked about the Israelite King, Solomon. "Solomon worshipped Astarte, the goddess of the Sidonians."

The Sidonians were a tribe of people who lived in what is now the country of Lebanon. Their goddess was Astarte, and the Israelite King Solomon worshipped her. Astarte was the daughter of Asherah, based on the fact that Astarte means fruit of the womb, and Asherah was the mother of the gods and goddesses. Now, Yahweh, the God of the Bible had a consort, and she had a daughter[30]. Yahweh was domestic!

The Israelites were not the only ones who worshipped Asherah. The Canaanites, who were the Nephilim that the Israelites conquered, called her Ashtoreth, and they worshipped her. The Babylonians may have called her Ishtar. There were 180 altars to Ishtar in ancient Babylon. And the Sumerians may have called her Inanna. So she's been around for a long time, but there seems to be confusion between Asherah's and Astarte's identities. Some sources said that Ishtar was Astarte, instead of Asherah.

Asherah was the mother of seventy gods. Seventy kids! She's like the old woman who lived in a shoe. I guess that's why she was considered a fertility goddess[31]. I didn't know what to make of this. Another Web site listed all of these gods: Marduk, god of the Babylonians; Ra, god of the Egyptians; Yahweh, god of the Israelites; Baal, god of the Canaanites; and Ashur, god of the Assyrians[32]. I guess they were the Elohim, the many gods. I wondered if any were also Asherah's children.

The *Book of Kings III,* Chapter 11:9, said that Yahweh was mad at King Solomon for worshipping other gods. "The Lord was angry with Solomon because his mind was turned away from the Lord God of Israel, who had appeared to him twice."

That brought up another twist. So, Yahweh appeared to Solomon twice, and appeared to Moses, Isaac, Jacob, and Abraham. Yahweh also had a consort and she had at least one daughter, whom Solomon worshipped. The logical conclusion is that Yahweh, and perhaps all of these gods and goddesses, were not invisible. They were flesh and blood beings! People saw them! And each god chose a different group of people as their own.

I lay on my uncomfortable military cot thinking about this. Ricky's words popped into my head: *How could God have a girlfriend?* Poor Ricky, he seemed so disturbed by this.

I had always thought Yahweh was the God of the Bible, the Father of Jesus, and the Creator of all things.

There still has to be a Creator of all things.

But was it Yahweh?

Thanksgiving

Camp Babylon was buzzing on Thanksgiving. President George Bush and the National Security Advisor, Condoleezza Rice, were in Baghdad! They were eating dinner with the troops. The television monitors around the base were covering it. It was on CNN and Fox News. That was a boost for the soldiers. We listened to their speeches and felt proud of the work we were doing[33].

A Catholic priest named Father Mike made a speech and said prayers before our dinner. Then I finally had a good meal: turkey, real gravy, stuffing, vegetables. It was great!

I sat next to Scoot and his friend Ma'ad, who had explained the Moslem term "People of the Book." It was very difficult, but I managed not to talk about Yahweh and Allah. It was Thanksgiving, time for a break. Although, Ma'ad would be the perfect person to talk to about Allah. I kept that thought in my cranium.

Yahweh and Allah II

I did not want to buy a Quran, the Moslem holy book, to find out about Allah. There are certain ways that it should be handled and stored, and I didn't think I could do that correctly. I'm not fond of rituals. I guess I don't have enough patience, and a lot of rituals don't make sense to me. Like holy water. How can water be holy? And if you put some on your forehead, then you are holy, too? I just don't understand these things. That's why carrying around a Quran the right way would be impossible for me. So, a lot of the information I have on Allah is through Ma'ad, the American Marine. Investigating Allah was a long process, just like Yahweh was. I'll try to just tell the highlights.

Ma'ad explained to me the basic beliefs of Islam. One of them is the saying "Allahu Akbar." "Allah" is the Moslem word for God. Akbar means the greatest. So, Allah is the greatest. The terrorists who flew the airplanes into the World Trade Center were shouting "Allahu Akbar" as the planes crashed. I asked Ma'ad what I thought was a simple question.

"Allah is the greatest what?"

Ma'ad seemed to become upset. "The greatest being," he said[34].

I don't think "greatest being" is what that saying originally meant. If the first Moslems always said, "Allah is the greatest," I think they were comparing Allah to the other gods and goddesses. Allah is the greatest god; greater than Yahweh, or Marduk, or Asherah, or Baal, or any other god or goddess. I don't think they meant the greatest being.

I asked Ma'ad how the Quran described Allah. He said Allah cannot be described, or even comprehended by us. Therefore, Allah is not described in the Quran. Muhammad wrote the Quran as it was dictated to him by the angel Gabriel. Gabriel did not describe God[35].

I found this interesting, since God is described in the Bible. Jesus said that He looked like His father in heaven, God. "When you see Me, you are seeing the One who sent Me." (*John* 12:45)

Moses claimed he saw the back of God in *Exodus* 33:23. The prophet Micaich saw "The Lord sitting on a throne" (*2 Chronicles* 18:18) So, according to the Bible, God looked like a man. But according to Ma'ad, the Quran does not describe God even one time in the whole book because we cannot comprehend God. That made sense to me. I don't think God looks like a man. However, I ran across a Web site that gave another reason why Allah was not described in the Quran.

The word Allah comes from an ancient Arabian title, *al-ilah*, which meant the "chief deity." The word deity means an object of worship, and is associated with enormous power. The "chief deity" of the ancient Arabians was the moon god, whose name was Sin. His symbol was the crescent moon. In Arabia, where the days are hot and oppressive and the nights are cool and bring relief, the people worshipped the moon god, Sin. He was called *al-ilah*, which later became Allah. He was their chief deity. Allah was not described in the Quran because the people of Arabia were already familiar with Allah. He was the moon god, Sin[36].

According to Ma'ad, the Moslems fast during the month that begins and ends with the appearance of the crescent moon in the sky. It is the ninth month of the Islamic calendar. For the next couple years it will begin in September. Ma'ad called that month Ramadan.

The crescent moon was Sin's symbol. Today it is Allah's symbol. Ma'ad also said God revealed the Quran during the month of the crescent moon[37].

In my opinion, it appears that Allah evolved like Yahweh did, from one of many gods to the only God, creator of all things. I didn't discuss my theory with Ma'ad. He seemed to take offense at any questioning of the beliefs of Islam.

I ran into Old One before I could finish my research. He was standing outside of the power station, just looking around. He saw me, and his lips turned up into a slight smile. I wondered if he was standing by the power station so he would run into me.

"Joy DiNardo, you have changed."

"Yes, my hair is one color now," I said in a mean way, then felt bad. "I'm not finished with my next answer. But, I know that Yahweh was the god of the mountains, and Allah was the god of the moon." I stopped to collect my thoughts. Old One waited patiently. "You were right; there were many gods, at least in the ancient world. But I was right, too. Today, Yahweh and Allah are considered the same God, the creator of all."

Old One looked exasperated. His slight smile turned to a frown. "It was Yahweh who commanded Nebuchadnezzar to destroy Jerusalem and Solomon's temple. He did this because the Israelites were worshipping other gods. Yahweh is a jealous God. It says that in your book."(Actually, it does say those exact words in *Exodus* 20:5. "Yahweh is a jealous God.") Old One looked as if he didn't want to say anything else, pausing for a minute before speaking again. "Yahweh and Allah are still fighting today over who is the greatest. That is why you are here in Babylon, Joy Di-Nardo."

Old One gave me a new question to answer: "What is the riddle of the Sumerians?" Then he also said something like "Find out where Yahweh got the Ten Commandments from."

Those were not his exact words. He seemed kind of stern and perturbed with me. I didn't know if I could buy what Old One said. I am in Babylon, Iraq, because Yahweh and Allah are continuing an ancient battle over who is the greatest God? If that's true, then we are all fighting, and we don't know what the fight is about. And where are Yahweh and Allah?

Anyway, I had a two-part assignment. It seemed interesting. I couldn't wait to begin working on these new questions.

The Sumerians
and the Ten Commandments I

There was celebrating on the base today. Iraqis training to be security policemen were shooting their guns in the air. Saddam Hussein had been captured in a "spider hole" in Northern Iraq! That was a nice Christmas present for everyone. It's interesting; some of these same Iraqis had been in Saddam Hussein's Jerusalem Brigade, training to invade Jerusalem. They used to walk around with maps of Jerusalem in their pockets. I've heard Saddam believed he was a reincarnation of Nebuchadnezzar, and one day, he would capture Jerusalem as Nebuchadnezzar had done. Now, his Jerusalem Brigade was celebrating his capture. On the news, they showed pictures of Iraqis celebrating in Baghdad and in Mosul. I had a good feeling about being here[38].

For Christmas, 2003, they had a special ceremony and dinner on the base. I ate with Lisa, and we were both feeling homesick. Christmas does that to you. It's the one time of year when you really should be at home. Right now, my family was gathered in Pennsylvania, exchanging presents and having fun: my sister with her husband and son from Pittsburgh, my other sister from New York with her fiancé and little dog, and my parents, my aunt and uncle, and some of my cousins.

Well, at least no one here is asking me if I'm "seeing someone special," or if I've "met any nice guys lately," or, "you're almost thirty, isn't it time to settle down and start a family?" I'm the oldest of three sisters, and I'm the only one without a "special guy," as my grandmother would say. They are worried that I'll be an old maid. That reminds me of the card game "Old Maid." The Old Maid's picture on her card was always a homely lady with pimples and goofy-looking hair. Joy DiNardo, the "Old Maid." My picture will be on the card, and on the box cover.

What if I don't want to get married? I have a career! These thoughts always ran through my head at strange times. *OK Joy, stop thinking and finish eating your food.*

After dinner, Lisa and I decided to go to the museum. Old One wouldn't be there today, so we could look around. They tightened security today. This would be a day that suicide bombers would like to attack—Christmas Day. Old One was not allowed on the base.

The museum sure had a lot of junk. It didn't seem to be very well organized. What has Old One been doing in here?

I began looking at a clay picture with Arabic writing below. I can read some Arabic. It was a replica of the Narmer Palette from the Cairo Museum. The Narmer Palette was from 3200 BC. It showed the Pharaoh Narmer (from Egypt) and some of his subjects making an offering to Narmer's father, the god Ra. It does not show the god Ra, only Narmer. The surprising thing is that Narmer is over twice the size of his subjects[39,40].

Narmer was a Nephilim, a giant, one of the sons of gods. He was the son of the god Ra. I think he was being depicted by the ancient Egyptian artist to be exactly as he looked. He was twice as tall as his subjects.

Remember in ancient Babylon, there was an eighteen-foot statue of a human-like figure? Could that have been a life-size statue of a Nephilim, or maybe even a life-size statue of a god?

Another clay picture showed Marduk, the god of Babylon. He was standing alone, dressed in capes and a tunic, as worn by kings. He had a long beard cut in a rectangle, like Old One's beard.

There was a statue of another person dressed in a tunic who had large eyes and a large, box-cut beard. The Arabic inscription below said it was a Sumerian depiction of Anu, god of the sky. This was from 3000 BC. Three more statues close by looked like this one, all with long beards[41].

I had a thought about these beards. When the Taliban had taken over Afghanistan, they made Afghan men grow long, scraggly beards. The explanation I heard was that they had to grow beards because Muhammad had a beard. But I think the beard tradition goes back to the Elohim, to Marduk, Anu, and the rest of them!

Maybe I think too much. I was supposed to be having fun looking around the museum with Lisa. Then I saw it—the Egyptian *Book of the Dead*!

"Lisa! It's the Egyptian *Book of the Dead*!

"What's that?" She wasn't very impressed. In fact, she didn't even glance over to see what it looked like.

"Lisa, it's the Egyptian book about what happens to you after you die. It was written thousands of years ago."

Lisa whirled towards me, making her long hair swirl over her face. "Joy, do you really think they knew what happened after someone died in ancient Egypt? They made dead people into mummies."

I stuck my tongue out, and Lisa gave me an exasperated look.

"I think they knew more than we do. Lisa, I have to read this book!"

Lisa looked at the book, then up at me. "It's not even in English. What language is this, Egyptian?"

"No, it's Arabic. Lisa, I'm taking this book."

"But Jo-oy, you can't just take it," Lisa whined.

"Yes I can. I'll bring it back."

Lisa tried to grab the book away from me. For a few seconds we were both pulling on it. Lisa and I can both be overly dramatic.

"Jo-oy, if you get caught, they'll arrest you. These things are ancient artifacts," Lisa whined again.

"Not this one, Lee-sa," I whined back, "It's just a replica. I'll bring it back in a couple of days."

Lisa let go of the book. "OK, OK, take it. You're nuts!" Then she said something in Spanish.

"Lisa, do you always have to be such a drama queen?"

"I'm just trying to keep you out of trouble, DiNardo."

I tucked the book under my shirt. I can't believe I just had to wrestle Lisa for the Egyptian *Book of the Dead*.

We walked out past the Polish soldier who was posted at the entrance, saying "Merry Christmas." The Polish soldier said "Merry Christmas." If he saw the book, he didn't say anything.

I was back on my uncomfortable military cot with the Egyptian *Book of the Dead*. I opened it. "Hymn to Osiris." He was the God of the underworld. I skimmed through the book. "The Chapter of Coming Forth by Day and of Living after Death." "The Chapter of Making a Man Return to Look upon His House on Earth." That's an interesting concept. Then I came to a chapter called "The Negative Confession." This title made me curious, so I began to read. Evidently, during the journey through the underworld, the dead person meets a bunch of Egyptian gods along the way. To each one of them, he must make one negative confession. I noticed that they seemed to be written mainly from a male's perspective. Here are some of them:

1. I have not committed sin.
2. I have not committed robbery and violence.
3. I have not stolen.
4. I have not slain men and women.
5. I have not uttered lies.
6. I have not cursed God.
7. I have not stolen the property of God.
8. I have not debauched the wife of any man. (This is said twice.)
9. I have not increased my wealth except through such things [as] are justly my own possessions.
10. I have not scorned the God of my town.
11. I have attacked no man.
12. I have not committed adultery. I have not lain with men[42,43].

I sat there in shock. Once again, an answer to Old One's question had found me. This was weird. Here are the Ten Commandments:

1. I am the Lord thy God, and thou shall not have other gods before me.
2. Thou shall not take the name of the Lord thy God in vain.
3. Remember to keep holy the Lord's Day.
4. Honor thy father and mother.
5. Thou shall not kill.
6. Thou shall not commit adultery.
7. Thou shall not steal.
8. Thou shall not bear false witness against thy neighbor.
9. Thou shall not covet thy neighbor's wife.
10. Thou shall not covet thy neighbor's goods[44].

THEY ALMOST MATCH! Most of the Ten Commandments are written in the negative form, just like the negative confessions in the Egyptian *Book of the Dead*.

Here's something else I found. The Egyptian *Book of the Dead* was written thousands of years ago; no one knows the exact date. The Ten Commandments were given to Moses by Yahweh around 1400 BC, give or take some years. Yahweh had helped Moses to lead the Israelites out of Egypt. Yahweh, Moses, the Israelites—all of them would have been familiar with the Egyptian *Book of the Dead*. So that's the answer! Yahweh took the Ten Commandments from the Egyptian *Book of the Dead*[45]!

I had to show Lisa. I ran over to Lisa's sleeping quarters, where I found her half-asleep. She was lying with a picture of her family on her pillow—mother, father, brother, and sister. Lisa was the oldest child. I looked at the picture for a minute. Her parents had come to Miami from Cuba. Her father was a doctor, and a handsome man. Her mother had beautiful, long, dark hair, like Lisa's.

I shook Lisa's shoulder. "Lisa, look at this."

"Joy, what the heck?" Lisa opened her eyes grudgingly.

"Lisa, you have to hear this. OK, these are from the Egyptian *Book of the Dead.*" I read to her the negative confessions. "OK, what do they sound like?"

"Um, sounds like Joy DiNardo on her first date with some guy. You know, Cable News Joy."

"No, Lisa. They sound like the Ten Commandments. Right?"

Lisa was quiet for a minute. Then she said, "Read those again." I read them again. "OK, yeah, a couple of them do. So what?"

"So what? Lisa, this is where Yahweh got the Ten Commandments from. The Egyptian *Book of the Dead.* See?"

Lisa's face slowly changed into a wise guy expression. "Right. I see," she said. "Was this before or after Yahweh went to India with Jesus?"

"Oh, real funny. No, Lisa, think about it. The Israelites were held captive in Egypt for hundreds of years. They were probably familiar with the *Book of the Dead.* Yahweh and Moses were too."

I think a light bulb went off in Lisa's head. She seemed to have a look on her face like she understood. Then the expression changed to a mean-girls look, and she said, "You don't have any proof of that."

"No, but it makes sense! Right?"

"Joy, go to sleep. You're a nut."

Lisa wouldn't admit it, but I know she agreed with me.

I decided to begin working on the Sumerians.

It was easy to find information about the Sumerians. There were tons of Web sites. Their civilization, Sumer, was the oldest civilization of humans. It was located right here in Iraq, between the Tigris and Euphrates Rivers. According to my Bible, the Garden of Eden was located somewhere along the Euphrates River too. This part of Iraq used to be called Mesopotamia.

In many ways, the Sumerians were just as advanced as we are today, and they existed in 4000 BC. Here are some achievements of the Sumerian civilization. Keep in mind that this was six thousand years ago:

The Sumerians invented the wheel. They had carts, chariots, and pottery making. The Sumerians used bricks for home building. They were the first to smelt iron.

They were the first to write. The Sumerians wrote in pictograph form first. (They drew little pictures for letters.) Later, they developed cuneiform writing. It's interesting that their language is not related to any other known language.

They developed a math system based on the number sixty. (Ours is based on the number ten.) We still use some of their math system. A clock has sixty minutes; a circle has 360 degrees.

They used algebra and geometry and were the first to have a calendar.

The Sumerians used leather for clothing and other items. They domesticated horses, sheep, cows, and other animals. Sumerian farmers crossbred wheat grains

They had a complex system of sewers and flush toilets to rid cities of waste and unhealthy effects of swamps. They had cemeteries. The Sumerians used gold and bronze to make things. They developed codes of law and rule by kingship[46].

Were all the Sumerians named Einstein? The list of firsts for the Sumerians goes on and on. Here's the weird part (there's always a weird part): the Sumerians knew there was an asteroid belt between Mars and Jupiter. The asteroid belt cannot be seen by the naked eye. Neither can Saturn, Uranus, Neptune, and Pluto. The Sumerians knew these planets existed. They did *not* have telescopes.

Pluto was not discovered by modern man until 1930. The Sumerians knew that Pluto existed in 4000 BC.

The Sumerians also listed one more planet beyond Pluto. They called it Nibiru. Some of our astronomers believe there is another planet beyond our known solar system. They call it Planet X. But I don't think they have found it yet with their high-powered telescopes.

The Sumerians had maps of constellations! How did they get this information?

The Sumerians built towering temples called ziggurats for their gods. Each city had a ziggurat and its own god. Nebuchadnezzar is quoted by Herodotus, the historian, as saying that he wanted the ziggurat of the god Marduk to be as grand as the ziggurat of Babel.

So the Tower of Babel did exist! That is amazing!

The Sumerians had a strong belief in life after death. They believed that each person has a ghost that follows the individual around at all times. I guess that's our soul.

The Sumerians had a whole list of gods. I was about to read the information on the Sumerian gods when Ricky burst into my sleeping quarters. He was so excited. Ricky never gets excited.

He was yelling "We're going to Giza for New Year's Eve! Giza, Egypt! To see the Great Pyramid!"

Giza, Egypt

Ricky managed to attach us (Ricky, Lisa, and me) to an Israeli tourist group. We went to Tallil, then to Tel Aviv, Israel, and then to Cairo, Egypt. Cairo is near Giza. I was nervous traveling in Egypt with an Israeli group. Tensions were high because of the Iraq War and the suicide bombings that had been going on in Israel. But we were treated well by our Egyptian travel hosts and guides. The Israelis were permitted to bring along their own security people.

At Giza, I purchased a book written in English called *The Nephilim and the Pyramid of the Apocalypse* by Patrick Heron[49]. It gave these facts about the Great Pyramid at Giza:

1. The Great Pyramid is located at the exact center of the earth. It is midway between the North Cape of Norway and the Southern Cape of South Africa. It is also midway between the West Coast of Mexico and the East Coast of China. It is on the intersection of the thirtieth parallel, both longitude and latitude. (I thought that was amazing. No one else did.)

2. The sides of the pyramid face exactly toward the true north, south, east, and west of the Earth. (So someone used the pyramid as a compass.)

3. The pyramid has 2.3 million blocks of stone. The lightest was 2.5 tons. Some weigh 50 tons. Huge granite blocks partway up the pyramid weigh 100 tons each. (How could the Egyptians have possibly built this? We couldn't build this today.)

4. The base of the pyramid is shaped in a square, with right angles that are accurate to within one twentieth of one degree.

5. The length of each side of the base of the pyramid is 365.2422 cubits, the exact number of days in a year. (How did the Egyptians know that?)

6. The slope of the pyramid is ten feet by nine feet, all the way up. If you multiply the height of the pyramid by ten to the ninth power, you get 91,840,000. That is about the number of miles from the Earth to the Sun. (That's not a coincidence. That was done on purpose. How did the ancient Egyptians know the distance to the sun?)

We were awestruck by the magnificence of the Great Pyramid. The travel host said the exterior was once covered in white limestone that reflected sunlight. This could be seen from miles around. Legend has it that the capstone was pure gold. Millennia of wear and tear have worn away the limestone and the gold capstone is gone. I had heard that the limestone was taken by Egyptians to use for buildings in Cairo.

They showed a movie to us about the construction of the pyramid. The movie narrator said it was not built by Hebrew slaves, as I had been taught. It was built by loyal Egyptians who lived in the area and donated their time in order to glorify the Pharaohs, the Egyptian rulers. The movie claimed that Egyptian stone masons carved the 2.5-ton to 50-ton rocks with stone chisels, and then moved them across logs used as rollers[50].

Ricky and Lisa sat there with numb expressions on their faces and believed all of that. There is no way! Ancient Egyptians did not make those calculations and build the Giza Pyramid with 50-ton rocks thousands of years ago! Hebrew slaves could not have built it either.

The Sphinx is next to the pyramid. It has a human face and the body of a lion. The movie said the Sphinx's face was that of a pharaoh. Pharaohs were gods and sons of gods. That's it! That's who built the Great Pyramid at Giza. The gods of Egypt—the Elohim.

I felt triumphant. Then I realized I didn't know who the Elohim were.

The Sumerians and the Ten Commandments II

It was hard to get back to the daily grind after being at the Great Pyramid in Egypt. There was something spiritual about being there. I wanted to go back instead of working at this old power station. New equipment was arriving from the States. We had to reconfigure everything to install the new equipment, and I was working twelve hours a day.

A rare thunderstorm one afternoon caused the plant to shut down operations. I went back to my uncomfortable military cot to take a nap, hoping it would rain all day so I could take a long one. Then I remembered the Sumerians. The Sumerian gods. I had been about to research the Sumerian gods when I was interrupted by Ricky.

I found some new information that was pretty wild:

Anu: He was the father of the gods. He lived in heaven with his wife.

Ninhursag: She was the mother of the gods on earth and the daughter of Anu. She was also a nurse. Her lover was Enki and probably a doctor. Here's the surprising thing: her nickname was Mammu, from which everyone on earth derived the names "mom," "momma," "mama," "mother," and so on.

Enki: He was a medicine man. I knew it—a doctor. He was also Anu's son, and Ninhursag's half brother—eeew! That's gross. Here's another surprising item. His symbol was two serpents intertwined on a staff. That is still the symbol today for modern medicine. It's called the winged caduceus. (I know. I'm a trivia nerd.) The intertwining serpents are also the symbol for DNA. According to my research, Enki created the first humans.

Enlil: He was another one of Anu's sons. Enlil was the supreme god on Earth. When the gods met in heaven, Enlil sat beside his father. He impregnated Ninlil, the grain goddess, by raping her. Their son was named Sin, the Moon god. Maybe that's where the word "sin" came from? Enlil then married Ninlil.

There were many other gods and goddesses: Marduk, Nabu, Nergal, Ningal, Inanna, and others. They were a very promiscuous group, all mating with each other and making more gods. Each had a temple, called a ziggurat, in Sumer[47,48].

Were these the Elohim, and where did they come from?

That evening, I ran into Old One again, walking past the museum.

"Hello, sir." I didn't know his real name. I considered asking it, but was still too intimidated.

"You have some information for me." He made a statement. He wasn't asking me.

"Well, yes, but I'm not finished. I can tell you what I have so far."

Old One just stood there and waited. I was starting to hate when he did that.

"Yahweh took the Ten Commandments from the Egyptian *Book of the Dead*. The riddle of the Sumerians is 'Where did they get their advanced civilization?' They knew all of the planets, crossbred wheat grains, had flush toilets, everything. I think the Elohim taught them. Also, the Elohim built the Great Pyramid at Giza. I just don't know who they were. The Elohim are mentioned in the Bible. I have to figure it out."

Old One kind of mumbled "You must learn in small amounts, in order to accept everything." His voice became louder. "Do not go too fast with the Elohim. But, I will help you. I will give you two names: Sodom and Gomorrah." He nodded his head, and then began walking into the museum. He stopped and looked back at me. "Return the book."

I still had the Egyptian *Book of the Dead*. How did he know that? *I will give you two names: Sodom and Gomorrah.* Then he walked away. I was beginning to grow weary of this. More research. More work. I needed to write down a list of everything I had learned from Old One just to organize my mind:

1. God located the Garden of Eden where there was gold.

2. There is no missing link. Humans were created somewhere by God and other beings about two hundred thosand years ago. Then God put man into the Garden of Eden to work.

3. There really were giants in Israel called Nephilim. They were the offspring of God's sons, whatever they were, and human women.

4. Yahweh commanded the Israelites to conquer the Nephilim, and they did.

5. I think Yahweh and Allah are Elohim, which are some kind of gods. They may have been fighting each other for hundreds, maybe thousands, of years.

6. The Elohim created the Sumerian civilization.

7. The Elohim built the Great Pyramid at Giza.

8. Yahweh took the Ten Commandments from the Egyptian *Book of the Dead*.

9. The real name of Jesus is Yahoshu, pronounced Yoshua or Yeshua. It means Yahweh saves.

10. Jesus spent His youth in India and countries east of Israel.

Seven months of work. At this time, I was really tired from working twelve-hour days. I didn't feel like finding out about Sodom and Gomorrah. I knew about them; they were sinful cities destroyed by whom? God? Yawheh? The Elohim?

Becky. That's it! I'd send this question to Becky. She'd get the answers for me. When I'm tired, I'm usually crabby. GRRRR. But I knew that tiredness wasn't the only thing making me crabby.

Crabby

I knew why I was crabby. My birthday was next week, February 12. The front number of my age was changing. The big *3-0*. The Old Maid was turning thirty. They're getting ready to put my picture on the card. It's really bad when the front number of your age changes. That's when you start to think about your life and to reevaluate things. What have I accomplished? Where am I going? Thoughts about mortality and life after death started to creep into my cranium. The Sumerians and the ancient Egyptians believed in life after death. That's a good sign!

As you can see, my mind was rambling. Also, I didn't know where Old One was going with all of this information. Who were the Elohim and the Nephilim? Why are humans the only species on Earth that did not evolve? We were created two hundred thousand years ago by God and someone else. How were we created? Why don't Christians believe the information about Jesus in India? Why did God care about gold? How does Old One know all of this? I e-mailed Becky.

Sodom and Gomorrah

My e-mail: *Hi Becky! I need information about Sodom and Gomorrah. Not the Bible story. Any other information that you can find. Anything unusual. Anything that relates to Sumer, or the gods of Sumer.*

Becky's e-mail: *Hi Joy! Got it. Should be interesting. By the way, happy birthday to you, happy birthday to you, happy birthday dear Joy. Happy birthday to you!*

I was a year older than Becky; she was still twenty-nine. I still hated Becky. (Just kidding.)

My contract period here in Iraq was beginning to wind down. I was scheduled to go home in July. What was I going to do then? I'd be thirty! Becky was already married and had a daughter. I didn't have anything. The mind really goes off of the deep end if you let it. At least, when I got home, I'd be with my family and friends again. But they were probably going to ask me when I will settle down and get married. Great!

It was Sunday so I decided to go to the base service and pray. That always helps. With God, you're never alone. God the Creator of All, that is. Not the Elohim.

I have always practiced my religion. I went to church every Sunday and prayed to God at night. I tried to be a good person and follow the teachings of Jesus. That's always been comforting to me.

On Monday we had a staff meeting. A Halliburton supervisor came from Baghdad. He stressed the fact that we should stay within the work triangle. Twenty-five Halliburton employees had been killed over the past year. Twenty-five! The fighting had continued since the invasion ended last March; mostly roadside bombs, suicide bombings, and kidnappings.

Sodom and Gomorrah

We were told that the terrorists would love to kidnap an American female and parade her in front of the television cameras. I was warned not to go anywhere alone. I thought about asking for a gun, but didn't know how to use one. I should have gone on those hunting trips with my dad. The problem is that I couldn't shoot a defenseless animal, let alone another person. Maybe this whole country was going to blow up—like Sodom and Gomorrah.

The story of Sodom and Gomorrah had always fascinated me. Sodom and Gomorrah were two cities located near the Dead Sea in Israel. According to the teachers in Bible school, they were noted for their sinful ways—wild sex orgies and degenerate behavior, kind of like Hollywood. Because of their sinfulness, God destroyed the cities by raining fire and brimstone down on them. I always wondered how God could do that—kill everyone. God is supposed to be merciful and forgiving.

The Bible version of Sodom and Gomorrah is a very disturbing story. It starts out with God and two angels talking to Abraham. (Abraham is the father of the Israelites and the Arabs.) God tells Abraham He is going to destroy the two cities because of the sins of their people. Abraham says there must be some good people in Sodom and Gomorrah. God should not destroy the good and bad together. After a bargaining session, God agreed that if He could find ten good people, He would not destroy the city. God sent two angels to find the ten good people. Abraham's nephew, Lot, met the angels at the gate of the city. Lot lived in Sodom. Somehow, he must have known the angels were coming. Lot convinced the angels to stay at his house, and he baked them unleavened bread. Before the angels fell asleep, all the men of the town surrounded the house. They called out to Lot, asking for the two angels so they could "know" them.

To "know" in the Bible sometimes means to have sexual relations. In *Genesis*, it said Adam "knew" Eve, and they had a child. I'm pretty sure that's what the townspeople meant, sexual relations, because Lot told them to take his two daughters instead. (What a nice guy!) The townspeople refused; they wanted the angels.

The townspeople pulled Lot out of the house, and so the angels struck the men "with blindness from the least to the greatest, so that they could not find the door." (*Genesis* 19:11)

The next morning, they told Lot to hurry with his family out of the city, for they would destroy it as God had sent them to do. They told Lot to take his family and go to the mountains. Lot wanted to go to the small city of Zoar and the angels agreed. The sun had risen when Lot entered Zoar. Then fire and brimstone rained down upon Sodom and Gomorrah. All the inhabitants were destroyed. Evidently, Lot's wife was lagging behind and had not yet entered Zoar. The Bible says she looked back as she fled and was turned into a pillar of salt.

Abraham woke up that morning and saw smoke, as from a furnace, in the direction of Sodom and Gomorrah. Then Lot became afraid to live in Zoar, so he went to the mountains with his two daughters. The daughters spoke among themselves. They said that there was not a man on the entire Earth remaining to come unto them and preserve the seed of their father. So they made their father drunk from wine and became pregnant by him. (They thought the whole world had been destroyed, except for them, according to *Genesis* 19:30-36.) The child of the older daughter was named Moab and became the father of the Moabites. The child of the younger daughter was named Ben-ammi and became the father of the children of Ammon.

This is a horrible story. Attempted rape of the angels, incest, and complete destruction of two cities. What I hadn't noticed before was the Bible said the angels, not God, destroyed Sodom and Gomorrah. I couldn't wait to get Becky's e-mail. My enthusiasm had returned! I think I'm done being a drama queen about my birthday. My moods change really fast, don't they?

I received Becky's e-mail later that week, and the only way I could describe it was stunning! Here are the main points.

Around 2000 BC, there was a war in the Middle East called the War of the Kings. One side consisted of the cities of Sodom, Gomorrah, Admah, Zebi'im, and Zoar. On the other side were Sumer, Ellasar, Goim, and Elam. This was mentioned in *Genesis*, Chapter 14. According to Becky:

1. The war was not because of a disagreement among the kings. It was really between two rival groups of the gods of Sumer, the Elohim. They used humans to fight each other. One group was comprised of the descendents of Enki. The other group was made up of Enlil and his offspring. (Remember them? The doctors? The gods of Sumer?) Sodom and Gomorrah were on the side of Enki's son, Marduk. Sumer and its allies were on the side of Enlil.

Side One	Side Two
Enki's Descendents	Enlil's Descendents
Sodom	Sumer
Gomorrah	Ellasar
Admah	Goim
Zebi'im	Elam
Zoar	

Enki's son, Marduk, had tried to take over the whole Middle East with human armies. That's why Enlil's group destroyed Sodom and Gomorrah and their allies. It had nothing to do with wicked people. Sodom and Gomorrah's sin was that they were against Enlil! Keep reading— Becky sent information that may prove this.

2. Sodom and Gomorrah are mentioned in an ancient Egyptian text, called the Nag Hammadi, as centers of learning, not cities of wickedness and sin. So they were not like Hollywood, according to the Nag Hammadi[51].

3. Much archaeological evidence supports the idea that the Elohim destroyed Sodom and Gomorrah by weapons that resemble our nuclear bombs of today, not by fire and brimstone[52].

In the 1920s, the Vatican Pontifical Biblical Institute investigated the area surrounding the southern end of the Dead Sea, where Sodom and Gomorrah were thought to have been located[53].

They discovered that settlements in the region were abruptly abandoned around 2000 BC and not reoccupied for several centuries after that. This may have been because of contamination. Springs around the Dead Sea have been found to be contaminated with radioactivity. It has caused infertility and various afflictions in humans and animals.

Hundreds of sulfur balls were found and collected in the area around the Dead Sea composed of pure powder sulfur. These types of sulfur balls are not found anywhere else in the world, including around volcanoes. They are not a natural occurrence.

Vitrified ash was found on the site. Vitrified ash is ash, dirt, and sand that had turned to glass. The same thing happened at Hiroshima and Nagasaki, Japan, where atomic bombs had exploded during World War II.

A skeleton was found completely turned to ash, except for the marrow, which was still visible. The same thing happened to skeletons at Hiroshima and Nagasaki.

The research team also found vaporized gold and oxidized bronze spearheads, which are consistent with an atomic explosion. Other ashen remains were found.

It appears that the cities had been vaporized. Not just Sodom and Gomorrah, but Admah and Zebi'im also. Only Zoar was not destroyed.

After the destruction of Sodom and Gomorrah, a radioactive cloud was created by the explosion. It traveled north and east to Sumer. The radioactive cloud caused the end of the Sumerian civilization! History shows that the Sumerian civilization had disappeared as mysteriously and suddenly as it appeared. Most of the people in Sumer died from radioactive poisoning. Becky said the information about the destruction of Sodom, Gomorrah, and Sumer is recorded in a Sumerian text called the *Erra Epos*. In Sumer "there was excruciating death to all living beings, people and animals alike, that withered plants and poisoned the waters."

But that's not the whole story. This was so interesting; I was trying to read faster than I could comprehend the words. Becky wrote about the two angels next:

1. The angels' names were Ninurta and Nergal. Ninurta was Enlil's and Ninhursag's son. Nergal was Enki's son who had turned against Marduk. According to the *Erra Epos,* they unleashed the weapons against Sodom and Gomorrah. Ninurta had an aerial battle craft that he used, called the Storm Bird by the Sumerians. These two angels, who were actually sons of Elohim, destroyed the sinning cities Sodom and Gomorrah. God did not.

2. Ninurta and Nergal also destroyed something in the Sinai desert. Ancient Babylonian texts called the *Khedorlaomer Texts* tell this story. There was a sacred place in the Sinai Desert called El-Paran, which meant "God's Gloried Place." Marduk's human army had tried to capture it, but was temporarily blocked by Abraham and his army at the entrance to the Sinai Desert. The entrance was called "Kadesh-Barnea." Whatever was in El-Paran was so sacred that Ninurta and Nergal destroyed it with their weapons, rather than have it captured by Marduk.

3. The devastation in the Sinai Desert was worse than Sodom and Gomorrah. An unnatural scarring of the Sinai Desert surface can be seen from pictures taken from modern spacecraft. The center of the Sinai Pen-

insula shows a great depressed area, a cavity. There are still, today, multitudes of scorched rocks covering the desert. Millions of blackened stones are strewn for tens of miles. The rocks are blackened only on the surface, consistent with the results of an explosion.

4. In the Sinai Desert and in Sumer, archaeologists have determined that there was an abrupt climate change around 2000 BC, bringing unexplained dryness and windblown dust storms. Could this be from the nuclear explosion[54]?

Probably the most interesting part of Becky's e-mail is about Abraham. In Bible school, we were taught that Abraham was a kindly old shepherd who could not have children with his wife, Sarah. So, as was the custom of that time, he had a child with his Egyptian maid, Hagar. Abraham and Hagar's son was named Ishmael. Ishmael's descendants became the Arabs. Later, Abraham was visited by angels, who told him Sarah would have a child. Abraham was one hundred years old at the time. Abraham and Sarah had a child who was named Isaac. Isaac's descendants became the Israelites. To test Abraham's loyalty, God asked Abraham to sacrifice (kill) Isaac on an altar. Abraham was about to sacrifice Isaac when God stopped him. He had proven his loyalty. The story of Abraham also includes God telling him that He is going to destroy Sodom and Gomorrah, and Abraham trying to talk God out of it. When you think about it, it's really a crazy story! Here's the rest of the information in Becky's e-mail about Abraham:

Abraham was not a kindly old shepherd. He descended from a line of priests, from the Sumerian City of Ur. His father's name was Terah. Abraham married his half-sister, Sarah. His nephew was named Lot. Abraham's father, Terah, had some connection to the Elohim. Some scholars believe he was one of them. (Becky wasn't sure about this.) Terah and Abraham moved from the city of Ur to Canaan. Abraham lived there until he was seventy-five years old, when the War of the Kings began. During the war, Abraham was given command of a small cavalry group that stopped Marduk from taking El-Paran in the Sinai Desert. The gods of Sumer had commanded him to do this. As a reward, the gods made a covenant with Abraham, promising him that his descendants would be given the land from the River of Egypt, the Nile River, to the Euphrates River in Iraq[55].

That territory now includes Israel, Jordan, Saudi Arabia, Lebanon, and parts of Egypt, Syria, and Iraq. That is amazing! Abraham's descendants are the Arabs and the Israelis. That is where they live today—the Promised Land, a land promised to both the Arabs and the Israelis.

Becky sent one more thing. She wrote that with the destruction of Sumer, most of the gods of Sumer, the Elohim, fled the area. That left Marduk and Babylon in control of the Middle East. Egypt was now the main rival of Babylon.

After reading all of this, I felt angry. Whoever the gods of Sumer were, they treated humans like cattle. They led them to slaughter in battles and wiped out whole cities with terrible weapons. That is the history of the Middle East, the history of Babylon and Iraq. All these people have ever known is killing, slaughter, and human sacrifices. It's going to be very difficult to make Iraq into a peaceful democracy like we're trying to do.

Who were the Elohim? They made a mess of the ancient world. I remembered seeing a statue of the god Marduk in the museum. He was an Elohim. He had one of those long beards, like Osama bin Laden.

If all of this was true, it was very different than the Bible version of Sodom and Gomorrah.

Old One said to take it slow with the Elohim. OK, for now, I guess I will. One thing was bothering me though. Abraham's son, Isaac, was born around 2000 BC. All of the Israelites descended from Isaac. A few hundred years later, at the time of the Exodus from Egypt, there were close to one million Israelites. Was that possible, in only a few hundred years? I had to talk to Old One.

The Hyskos

On February 12, Ricky and Lisa tried to sing Happy Birthday to me at dinner. They put candles in my instant mashed potatoes.

Two days later, it was Valentine's Day. That was just great, the big 3-0, and then no Valentine. I'm on a military base, and I didn't get one Valentine, no chocolates, nothing. They should do away with Valentine's Day because it's too aggravating.

At least I received an e-mail from my sister Kim in New York. She's a PR person for a fashion magazine. We all have cute little names in my family: Joy, Kim, June. Kim, June, Joy. June, Joy, Kim.

Kim said she had to do some research about the origin of eye makeup for a Valentine's Day promotion and discovered that wearing eye shadow and eyeliner started in Iraq, in the city of Sumer. The legend is that gods came down to earth and showed human women how to make themselves more attractive by using makeup around the eyes. Then the gods were so attracted to the human women that they married them. Since I'm in Iraq, where Sumer was, she thought I would find it interesting. I'm at the birthplace of fashion!

I stared at the e-mail. Kim may have stumbled on more evidence about the sons of gods who married human women. It's weird the way this information is coming to me. I stored that e-mail in the back of my brain for future use.

For the next week, I tried to find Old One at the museum. He didn't show up for work and I was beginning to get worried about him. At dinner, I asked Ricky and Lisa my question about Isaac and the Israelites. I think Isaac married someone named Rebecca, and then a few hundred years later close to one million of their descendants escaped from Egypt[56]. How is that possible?

Lisa thought for a moment. Her forehead wrinkled like it always does when she's thinking. "Actually, that's possible. They need to double every twenty-five to thirty years. It could have happened."

I started doubling in my head—$2X2=4X2=8X2=16X2=32$, and so on. After twenty doublings, I was up to 1,048,576 people. In six hundred years, if they doubled every twenty-five years, there would be twenty-four doublings. So, they could get to one million.

Ricky was making faces while we were doubling. He was moving back and forth in his chair like he wanted to say something. Finally, he asked, "Do you know what happened to the Israelites between the time of Isaac and the Exodus from Egypt?"

I looked at Lisa. She rolled her eyes and I think we had the same thought—here we go again, Professor Ricky.

"Um, somehow they ended up as slaves in Egypt," I answered.

Ricky shook his head. "Let me explain this. First of all, Isaac's name was changed to Israel. *Isra* means "soldier," and *El* means "God" in Hebrew. So, Isaac's name was changed to "soldier of God.""

"God was Yahweh, right?" I interrupted.

"Right. So, the Israelites were named after Isaac. They were the soldiers of God, Yahweh." Ricky paused. I guess he thought I would make a comment, but I didn't.

"Yahweh told Abraham, Isaac's father, to take his family to Egypt. They began traveling south through Canaan to Egypt, but it took several generations. Finally, they reached the city of Goshen in Egypt.

I interrupted again. "Why did it take so long?"

Ricky looked perturbed. "I don't know. Do you have to ask questions?"

"I can't help it. It's hard for me not to talk."

"Just pay attention," Ricky said with a sigh, "The rabbis didn't let me ask questions."

"OK."

Ricky began again. "At first, the Israelites lived well in Egypt. But then a new pharaoh came to the throne. The new pharaoh was worried about foreign peoples living in Egypt. His main concern was a group of people called the Hyksos. The Hyksos came from Sumer and other areas of western Asia. They were a mixed group of people who did not assimilate into

Egyptian society. They took over portions of lower Egypt and even massacred some of the native Egyptians." Ricky paused and took a sip of his milk carton. I wasn't allowed to ask questions, so I waited silently while he sipped his drink. Lisa put her head in her hands.

"The Hyksos brought slaves from Nubia with them. Nubia was a country to the south of Egypt. So there was a general outcry against foreigners by the Egyptians. At that point, the pharaoh enslaved the Israelites and treated them very cruelly. They were kept together in one area and not permitted to travel throughout Egypt." Ricky paused again. He took another sip from his milk carton. This was getting tedious.

"The Hyksos and the Israelites were related racially, probably because of their Sumerian roots. Some of the Hyksos had Semitic names, like the Israelites. Semitic refers to any Middle Eastern descendants of Noah's son, Sem."

I couldn't keep quiet any more. "Which pharaoh enslaved the Israelites?"

"Pharaoh Amosis. He led the Egyptians in a campaign to rid the country of the Hyksos. Many of the Hyksos were slaughtered or chased out of the country. Others were enslaved and probably mixed in with the Israelites. That's why there were close to one million Israelites that escaped from Egypt. They were mixed with the Hyksos. Not that goofy doubling thing you two lame brains were doing[57,58]."

Lisa slammed her hands on the table. "Lame brains? You know, I have severely hurt people for much less of an insult than that."

"I feel like dumping the rest of your stupid milk on your head," I chimed in.

"Notice he said *probably* mixed with the Hyksos. He doesn't know for sure," Lisa added

"Yeah, because he was too afraid to ask the rabbis any questions in school."

Ricky finally got a word in. "I'm leaving. You guys don't recognize genius when it's right in front of you." He started to rise, but sat back down when I grabbed his arm.

"Ricky, wait, before you go, let me finish the story."

He shook his head. "It is finished."

I shook my head back. "No, then Yahweh and Moses led the Israelites out of Egypt. They stayed in the Sinai Desert for many years. Then, led by Joshua, they killed all of the Nephilim in Canaan. Yahweh told them to do that. So they took over Canaan. They built a great temple in Jerusalem to honor Yahweh. Yahweh became angry with them because they still continued to worship other gods, so he made King Nebuchadnezzar of Babylon attack them. Nebuchadnezzar captured the Israelites and took them back to Babylon." I looked at Ricky. "Then, what happened in Babylon?"

He stood up, ready to leave. "OK, here's the *Reader's Digest* version." (That meant the short version.) "They wrote the rest of the Torah and were allowed to return to Jerusalem after seventy years, after the Persians defeated the Babylonians. After that, Israel was conquered by many invaders: Alexander the Great, whose father was a god, the Romans, the Persians, and many others. The Israelites were scattered all over the world until 1948 when the country of Israel was established. Now, they are back in the Promised Land."

"And we are in Babylon," Lisa said, almost to herself.

The Birth of Yahoshu I

It was already March when Old One finally returned to the museum. I had returned the Egyptian *Book of the Dead*. I also had a lot of time to think. Everything that happened in the Middle East from 4000 BC to the birth of Jesus was because of the gods of Sumer. And everything that happened was violent and horrible.

I said that to Old One. I knew the true story of Sodom and Gomorrah. The people of the Middle East were the toys of the Elohim. Who were the Elohim?

Old One seemed to get a painful expression on his face as I spoke. He hesitated and then stuttered a bit as he replied. He was holding something back from me. Old One said I am not ready yet. The Truth is coming to me. It is in the future. "Study the birth of Yahoshu." I felt like genuflecting or something as I left. *Study the birth of Yahoshu*. OK.

March 11, 2004

March 11, 2004 was a bad day at the base. Terrorists had bombed a train station in Madrid, Spain. Around two hundred people were killed. There was a small Spanish contingent at Camp Babylon. The Spaniards were glued to the television monitors.

A couple of days later, the Spanish government announced they were going to pull their troops out of Iraq in June. They believed that would protect them from further terrorist attacks. Everyone at the base believed pulling out would only make things worse. If the terrorists can get what they want by bombing, they will do it again and again. It was demoralizing to everyone on the base to hear the Spanish would be leaving[65].

That will make it worse for us in Iraq, I thought. The terrorists will increase their bombing and kidnapping if they have a victory. Since September 11, 2001, they have had nothing but defeats: the overthrow of the Taliban in Afghanistan, the capture or killing of Al Qaeda leaders, Osama bin Laden in hiding, the overthrow and capture of Saddam Hussein, the shutting down of terrorist training camps everywhere, and defeats in the Philippines. Now, they have a victory in Spain[66].

The Birth of Yahoshu II

I was feeling down because it seemed like the terrorists were winning. People who came here to help were being killed. I had to stay in a triangular work area. About two hundred people were just murdered in Madrid. I turned to what has made me feel better so many times before: my Orthodox Bible and my uncomfortable military cot. I thought about Old One, yes, Old One. Let's see, study the birth of Yahoshu, Jesus, the Messiah. The first thing that came to mind was the prophecy that the Messiah would come from the House of King David. Jesus would be a descendant of King David of Israel.

I decided to look up Yahoshu's ancestors. The lineage of Yahoshu, Jesus, is in the Bible. Both *Matthew* and *Luke* give a list of Jesus' ancestors in the New Testament and they don't agree with each other, either:

LUKE	MATTHEW
God	
Adam	
Seth	
Enos	
Cainan	
Malaleel	
Jared	
Enoch	
Mathusale	
Lamech	

Noah	
Sem	
Arphaxed	
Cainan	
Sale	
Eber	
Phalec	
Ragau	
Seruch	
Nacor	
Terah	
Abraham	Abraham
Isaac	Isaac
Jacob	Jacob
Judas	Judas
Phares	Phares
Esron	Esron
Aram	Aram
Aminadab	Aminadab
Naasson	Naasson
Salmon	Salmon
Booz	Booz
Obed	Obed
Jesse	Jesse
DAVID	DAVID
Nathan	Solomon
(Nathan is Solomon's Brother)	(From here they are different)
Matthata	Roboam
Menna	Abia
Melea	Asa
Eliachim	Josephat
Jona	Joram
Joseph	Ozias
Judas	Joatham

Simeon	Achaz
Levi	Ezechias
Matthat	Manasses
Jorim	Amon
Eliezer	Josoas
Jesus (Not Christ)	Jechonias
Her	
Elmadam	
Cosam	
Addi	
Melchi	
Neri	
Salathiel	Salathiel
Zorobabel	Zorobabel
Resa	Abuid
Joanna	Eliachim
Joda	Azor
Josech	Sadoc
Semei	Achim
Matthathias	Eluid
Maath	Eleazor
Nagge	
Esli	
Naum	
Amos	
Matthathias	
Joseph	
Janne	
Melchi	
Levi	
Matthat	Matthan
Heli	Jacob
Joseph	Joseph
Jesus	Jesus

There it was. The lineage of Yahoshu, Jesus, as presented by *Luke* and *Matthew*, and most of it didn't agree. *Luke* started with God and Adam, and *Matthew* started with Abraham. Many of the names are different. Dueling genealogies, like the dueling banjos in the movie *Deliverance*. The "Dueling Banjos" song from *Deliverance* started going through my head. It's one of those songs that won't leave. "Dueling Banjos." Jesus, lineage in *Luke*--"Dueling Banjos." Jesus, lineage in *Matthew*--"Dueling Banjos." It's a catchy tune at first. Then it gets aggravating. More "Dueling Banjos." I tried to think of another song. I always liked "Walking on Sunshine." I forced my mind to hear that song. "I'm walking on sunshine, well, walking on sunshine."

Then I realized that I was weird. I was sitting there forcing myself to think of the "Walking on Sunshine" song while I reviewed the lineage of Jesus in the New Testament. I needed therapy.

OK, why were these lists so different? They were the same from Abraham down to David. There's someone named Booz three names ahead of David! Do you think he had a drinking problem? "Hi, I'm King David. This is my great-grandfather, Booz. He owns a vineyard in Jerusalem. One thousand BC was a good year for wine." Some Bibles spell the name as Boaz. That's better than Booz.

OK, I needed to be serious.

The first difference exists because *Luke* was trying to establish that Jesus came from God. So he lists Jesus' ancestors all the way back to Adam and God. *Matthew* didn't do that. Now why did *Luke* want to go all the way back to Adam and God? I knew the answer to that one. It involves the Garden of Eden. The Serpent, whoever that was, tricked Eve into eating the fruit of the Tree of Knowledge. God was angry, and He said the following to the Serpent: "I will put enmities between thee and the woman, and thy seed and her seed: she will crush thy head, and thou shall lie in wait for her heel." (*Genesis* 3:15)

In Bible school, they told me this passage was the first prediction of the Messiah. So *Luke* was demonstrating that Jesus was the seed of Eve who would crush the Serpent. Therefore, he showed the ancestors of Jesus all the way back to Adam and God.

I also knew that *Matthew* wanted to show Jesus was of the royal Hebrew bloodline. He wanted to convince everyone that Jesus was the King of the Jewish people. That's why he began with Abraham, the father of the Jewish people.

Luke's and *Matthew's* lists agree from Abraham until King David, where they become different again. *Matthew* showed King Solomon next, after King David. *Luke* showed Solomon's brother, Nathan, after King David. Why would they do that?

This question called for the Internet. I lit up my laptop and logged on. There were many Web sites about the lineage of Jesus. Many of them were authored by atheists or people who were anti-Christian, claiming the different lineages prove the Bible was incorrect: full of discrepancies, made up stories, and lies. But there had to be something to this. Why would both lists of the lineage of Jesus be included in the New Testament if one of them was wrong?

I stumbled across an interesting Web site that explained everything. This Web site, by Dr. Henrietta Mears and Guy Cramer, claimed that Mary and Joseph were cousins[59]. That made sense. It explained why Joseph was chosen to be Mary's husband. He wasn't just some old guy who lived nearby; he was Mary's cousin.

The Web site also said Nathan was Mary's ancestor. (Nathan was King Solomon's brother on *Luke's* list.) *Luke* presented Mary's ancestors from Nathan, all the way down to Heli, before Joseph. *Luke* probably thought it was appropriate to show Mary's family because of the virgin birth. *Matthew* showed Joseph's ancestors from Solomon, all the way to Jesus.

It was interesting that both *Luke's* and *Matthew's* lineages showed Salathiel and Zorobabel as ancestors of both Mary and Joseph. Salathiel and Zorobabel lived when the Israelites were in Babylon. *Luke* and *Matthew* showed different fathers for Salathiel. It was obvious that *Luke* was correct. *Matthew* skipped six ancestors of Salathiel. There was a great deal of writing on the Internet about how this proved that the Bible lineage was incorrect.

In my opinion, it didn't matter. Salathiel and Zorobabel were descendants of David. So either way, both Mary and Joseph were from the House of David.

Luke should have put Mary at the end, instead of Joseph. It's that Adam's rib thing again. He did not want to include a woman in the lineage.

Here's something pretty amazing from that same Web site. Five hundred years before the birth of Jesus, Zechariah, the prophet, made a prediction about who would mourn the Messiah when He was killed. This was from *Zechariah* 12:14: "And the land shall mourn, every family by itself; the family of the house of David...the family of the house of Nathan...the family of the house of Levi...the family of the house of Semei."

All four of these names were on Mary's lineage list! Zechariah predicted that the Messiah would come from Mary's line, which included King David. That was pretty amazing to me.

So Yahoshu, Jesus, was a descendant of King David, through both Mary and Joseph. Mary and Joseph were cousins.

I think that I need to find out more about Mary.

I looked through my Bible, but there wasn't much information about Mary before the birth of Jesus. I looked through *Matthew, Mark, Luke,* and *John,* and came up with nada, nothing. So I did a search on my computer for Mary before the birth of Jesus. It came up with a document called the "Apocryphon," sometimes called the Apocrypha. This was a collection of writings that the early Christian church leaders decided to leave out of the Bible. It included such writings as *The Gospel of Thomas, The Gospel of Mary,* (Mary Magdalene), *The Infancy Gospel of James,* and others. My computer directed me to *The Infancy Gospel of James*[60]. It began with a story about Mary's parents.

Mary's father was called Joachim, and was also known as Heli. Mary's mother was named Anna.

Mary's parents were happy and wealthy. According to *The Infancy Gospel of James,* they always gave one-third of their income to the temple. However, they were not able to have children, and this was a great embarrassment to them.

Evidently, there was one special day when everyone went to the temple to offer gifts to the Lord. When Joachim tried to offer his gifts, someone named Rueben "stood over against him saying: 'It is not lawful for thee to offer thy gifts for as much as thou has gotten no seed in Israel.'" Joachim could not present his gifts because he had no children.

Joachim must have been an emotional guy, because the next thing he did was run off into the wilderness, and pitch a tent, and fast for forty days and forty nights. He said he would not eat or drink until God visited him.

Anna was emotional too. She sent her handmaiden away and bewailed herself with two bewailings: one for her widowhood because her husband disappeared into the wilderness and another for her childlessness. The two of them made quite a scene, according to *The Infancy Gospel of James.*

The next thing that happened was surprising to me. Anna took off her mourning garments. I guess she was wearing mourning garments because

80

she was bewailing. Then she cleansed her head and put on her bridal garments. About the ninth hour, she went into the garden to walk and sat down under a Laurel tree, looking up to heaven and bewailing again. An angel of the Lord appeared, saying: "Anna, Anna, the Lord hath hearkened unto thy prayer, and thou shalt conceive and bear, and thy seed shall be spoken of in the whole world." Anna pledged the baby to the service of God.

OK, so far so good. Now the strange part, or should I say the *stranger* part: the text said two messengers came to Anna. Not angels, but messengers. They told Anna that Joachim will be coming with his flocks because an angel had told Joachim that Anna conceived.

According to the text, Joachim told his herdsmen to bring the following: ten lambs without blemish—they would be for the Lord; twelve tender calves for the priests and elders; and one hundred kids (goats) for the whole people. Joachim was preparing a feast of celebration.

Something very strange just happened here! Anna conceived while Joachim was in the wilderness fasting. The only person that Anna was with was an angel.

So was the angel the father?

Joachim wasn't upset about this. He was happy and preparing a feast.

OK, in other ancient texts, the Elohim are referred to as angels. Was Mary's father an angel, an Elohim, a god? Is that why there was such a great feast? Is that why Anna pledged the baby, Mary, to the service of God? Is that why Anna put on her wedding dress and went into the garden?

The story continues with the angel going to Joachim and telling him that Anna had conceived. It must be that Anna conceived with an Elohim. And the Lord was attending the feast. The lambs were for him!

You will see later that the way Anna and Joachim treated Mary makes this more believable. But first, here's what I found out about Anna's ancestry.

Anna was the daughter of Matthan, who was a high priest. If you look on the lineage chart under Matthew, Matthan is Joseph's grandfather. So Anna and Joachim were cousins. And Anna descended from King David also. So, even with an Elohim father, Mary was still from the line of King David, through Anna. That may also be why Joseph, Mary's cousin, was chosen to be Mary's husband. Of course, this is all just my opinion, but it makes sense. It will make more sense as we go along here.

The Easter Movie

It was Easter Sunday in Babylon. This year, it fell on April 11. They had been trying to get the movie *The Passion of the Christ* to show on the base. The movie had been breaking attendance records in the States, and a lot of the soldiers wanted to see it. I did, too, but they weren't able to get it for us. Instead, they had the movie *King of Kings*. This was about the main events of Jesus' life. Ricky and Lisa didn't want to go so I went to see it by myself, sitting in front of a man and a woman who I think were reporters. At least they sounded like it by some of the things they said. I hadn't seen them before on the base.

There is an absolutely magnificent scene in the movie that depicts the "Sermon on the Mount," my favorite teaching. Jesus is played by Jeffrey Hunter, who looks majestic as he gives the sermon. He seems to tower above the crowd as he speaks. In the movie, he has long brown hair and an almost reddish beard. His eyes appeared grayish-blue and sparkling. He seemed to be glowing and bright as he spoke. His voice was strong yet gentle, full of compassion. The scene was fabulous. I was thoroughly enjoying this, and then she said it—the reporter—"Jesus didn't really look like that. He was probably short with dark curly hair and a long beard. He probably had an olive complexion and small dark eyes. The Hebrews in the year AD 30 didn't look like that guy."

She couldn't let me enjoy the scene, my favorite movie scene! The other reporter agreed with her. He said, "This is an older movie. It shows the prejudices of the times." (The movie was made in 1961.)

At first I thought, yes, they are probably right. Jesus probably didn't look like Jeffrey Hunter. He probably didn't look so magnificent. Then, I began to get one of those ideas that creeps into the brain from the back, covers the top, and then takes over the whole brain. Jesus' grandfather was a god of Sumer, an Elohim! Anna, Mary's mother, had conceived with an Elohim. First of all, the gods of Sumer, the Elohim, were of taller stature than the rest of us. So, Jesus would be tall, taller than the disciples and townspeople He was speaking to. Second, the statues of the gods in the museum did not have dark, curly hair and small, dark eyes. The statue of the god Anu had long, wavy, light brown hair and his eyes were unusually large. If I remember correctly, they were gray. Anu's skin was fair—at least on the statue I saw. He did not have an olive complexion. So, if this is what the Elohim looked like, then Jesus may have looked like Jeffrey Hunter.

I left the movie. I had to prove right now that the reporters didn't know everything like they thought they did. See how I get obsessed with things?

I started my Internet research again, coming across this surprising information:

1. In the Gnostic Christian writing called the "Shepherd of Hermas," it referred to the lofty stature of the Son of God. (The Gnostics were an early Christian sect.) The "Shepherd of Hermas" was written somewhere around AD 120 to 150.

2. A Roman governor of Judea named Publius Lentullus wrote a report to the Roman Senate that included information about Jesus. It said: "There appeared...a man of the Jewish nation, of great virtue, named Yeshua...He raised the dead and cureth all manner of diseases. A man of stature somewhat tall and comely...His hair the color of the chestnut...His face without spot or wrinkle...His beard thickish, in color like his hair...His eyes gray, clear, and quick." The Web site said the authenticity of this letter hasn't been established conclusively.

3. Pontius Pilate wrote a letter to Tiberius Caesar. Copies of this letter are in the Congressional Library in Washington, D.C.: "One day I observed in the midst of a group of people a young man who was leaning against a tree, calmly addressing a multitude. I was told it was Jesus. This I could easily have suspected so great was the difference between him and those who were listening to Him. His golden colored hair and beard gave to his appearance a celestial aspect[67]."

I found this letter posted on a few Web sites. No one seemed to be challenging its authenticity.

4. There is a manuscript called the *Archko Volume*. It contains court records from Judea in the days of Jesus. According to the Web site, copies

of this manuscript were found in the Library in Constantinople and in Roman Senatorial Documents kept in the Vatican. In a section of the manuscript entitled "Gamaliel's Interview," it said of Jesus: "If you ever meet Him, you will know Him…there is something that distinguishes Him from every other man. He is the picture of His mother…His hair is a little more golden than hers…He is tall…and of swarthy complexion, though this is from exposure. His eyes are large and a soft blue."

I didn't see anything that questioned the authenticity of this document, either. According to "Gamaliel's Interview," Mary's hair was somewhat golden, also.

5. I remembered what Mena had said in Afghanistan. St. Issa (Jesus) was immediately recognized by the Jains (they are Indians) as one who had received the mercy of the Lord. So now I know what that means. They immediately recognized Jesus because He looked like an Elohim, a god, the Lord. That's what they meant by "one who received the mercy of the Lord[68]."

6. Mena also said that when St. Issa came to Juggernaut, India, the white priests of Brahma made him a joyous welcome. Why would they celebrate the appearance of a thirteen-year-old boy from Israel? Because He looked like an Elohim—a god of Sumer[69]!

7. Jesus said, "When you see Me, you are seeing the One who sent Me." (*John* 12:45) He looked like a god.

I wanted to tell the know-it-all reporters about this. I wrote everything down on a sheet of paper. I thought maybe I shouldn't include the parts about the gods of Sumer. If they are not familiar with the Sumerians, they won't understand this. I included them.

I walked back to the movie tent. The movie was over, but the female reporter was still inside. I handed her what I had written down and walked away, fast. I couldn't think of anything to say. That happens sometimes when I get passionate. She probably thought I was from another planet. Anyway, I did it!

The Birth of Yahoshu III

The story of Mary continued in the *Infancy Gospel of James*.

When Mary was six months old, her mother stood her upon the ground to see if she would walk. She took seven steps. Then, Anna caught her up and said "thou shalt walk no more upon this ground until I bring thee into the temple of the Lord." She called for the daughters of the Hebrews that were undefiled and "they carried her hither and thither."

When Mary was one year old, Joachim held a great feast, bringing the child to the priests who blessed her. When Mary was two, Joachim wanted to take her to the temple to fulfill Anna's promise that the child would be a servant of God, but Anna decided to wait one more year.

When Mary was three, her parents left her with the priests in the temple. The *Infancy Gospel of James* said "Mary was in the temple of the Lord as a dove that is nurtured: and she received food from the hand of an angel."

So she was fed something special by an angel, which is an Elohim? Could this have been in preparation for becoming the mother of Jesus? This went on until Mary was twelve. Then things became very crazy, according to the *Infancy Gospel of James*.

The priests were afraid Mary would pollute the sanctuary of the Lord. My guess was that the priest believed Mary was about to begin her menstrual cycles. The priests didn't know what to do, so the high priest put on the vestment with twelve bells and went into an area of the temple called the Holy of Holies. That must have been where the Elohim stayed, because he was met by an angel. The angel told the high priest what to do: assemble all of the men who are widowers. Let them all bring a rod. Whomsoever the Lord will show a sign, Mary will be his wife.

All the men who were widowers gave rods to the high priest. He took the rods into the temple and prayed. He came back out and handed the rods back. A dove came out of Joseph's rod and flew upon his beard. That was the sign.

Now, I know a dove did not fly out of a rod, so I don't know what that meant. I guess it doesn't matter. Joseph was chosen. (In the *Arabic Gospel of the Apocryphon*, it says "the dove flew onto his rod." That makes more sense.)

Joseph objected to the high priest. He didn't just object, he refused, saying he would be a laughing stock because he is an old man and Mary is a girl. The priest reminded Joseph about what happened to others who disobeyed the Lord. Joseph became afraid, and so he agreed to be Mary's husband. He said to Mary, "Lo, I have received thee out of the temple of the Lord; and now do I leave thee in my house, and I go away to build my buildings and I will come again unto thee. The Lord shall watch over thee."

So, Joseph put Mary in his house and then left. ·

In the meantime, the priest wanted to make a veil for the temple. It could only be made by virgins. Mary was one of the virgins chosen to make the veil. She was chosen to weave the purple and scarlet sections. She took the material back to Joseph's house and began to spin it. Now here is where the *Infancy Gospel of James* describes how Jesus was conceived. For the most part, it agrees with the gospels of *Matthew* and *Luke* in the New Testament.

Mary took a pitcher and went forth to fill it with water. She heard a voice that said "Hail, thou art full of grace, the Lord is with thee: blessed art thou among women." Mary could not tell where the voice came from and began to tremble. She went back into the house, sat down, and drew out the thread. Then an angel stood before her, saying "Fear not, Mary, for thou hast found grace before the Lord of all things, and thou shalt conceive of His word."

Mary replied, "Shall I verily conceive of the living God, and bring forth after the manner of all women?"

Let's stop here for one minute. Living God? Was that an Elohim? Mary was familiar with the Elohim. They had fed Mary in the temple. She asked if she would conceive by an Elohim in the manner of all women. Does that mean there was another way to conceive, other than the usual way? The answer from the angel was difficult to understand.

"Not so, Mary, for a power of the Lord shall overshadow thee: wherefore also that holy thing which shall be born of thee shall be called the Son of the Highest. And thou shalt call his name Immanuel; for He shall save his people from their sins."

Mary said, "Behold the handmaid of the Lord is before him: be it unto me according to thy word."

Unfortunately, none of the texts I have read describe what happened next in the house. But here's something that gives us a hint. The *Infancy Gospel of James* said later on Mary finished the purple and scarlet, and brought it to the high priest. The high priest blessed her and said, "Mary, the Lord God hath magnified thy name, and thou shalt be blessed among all generations on earth."

The priest knew what had happened. He knew Mary had conceived, by the Lord God Yahweh. That's why he said she shall be blessed among all generations. Also, the priest did not reject the purple and scarlet that Mary had woven. The purple and scarlet had to be made by a virgin. So the high priest believed that Mary had conceived by the Lord God Yahweh, but was still a virgin.

The angel had said to Mary "a power of the Lord will overshadow thee." That's how the angel described how Mary would become pregnant. What does overshadow mean? The only thing that comes to mind is being put to sleep. If you overshadow something, you are putting it in darkness. When you go to sleep, you are in darkness. So, was Mary put to sleep and then artificially impregnated? That way, she would still be a virgin. That was the other way Mary could conceive. It was not in the manner of all women.

At first, this sounds ridiculous. I could just picture Lisa laughing at me right now. Artificially impregnated! Her shoulders would be heaving up and down like they usually do. Lisa looks like a volcano when she laughs. Ricky would just give me that look of pity.

But if the Elohim could build the Great Pyramid at Giza, create the Sumerian civilization, and map the constellations, they probably knew about artificial conception. I wished I knew where the Elohim came from. Were they the remnants of some ancient, lost civilization, like Atlantis? Were they extraterrestrials? I wished Old One would just tell me.

The story in the *Infancy Gospel of James* continued. After the priest blessed Mary, she went to the house of her cousin, Elizabeth, who was six months pregnant with John the Baptist. It said that when Elizabeth saw

Mary, she blessed her and said: "Whence is this to me that the mother of my Lord should come unto me? For behold that which is in me leaped and blessed thee." Elizabeth knew Mary had conceived by the Lord Yahweh. "And Mary forgat the mysteries which Gabriel the archangel had told her…and she abode three months with Elizabeth."

So, the angel that came to Joseph's house was Gabriel. He was the same one that dictated the Quran to Muhammad.

After Mary left Elizabeth's house, she went back to Joseph's house and hid herself. In her sixth month, Joseph returned home. It said he found her great with child, so he smote his face and cast himself down upon the ground on sackcloth and wept bitterly. He said "who hath done this evil in mine house and hath defiled the virgin? Why hast thou this? Thou hast forgotten the Lord thy God. Why hast thou humbled thy soul, thou that wast nourished up in the Holy of Holies and didst receive food at the hand of an angel?"

Mary wept bitterly, saying "I am pure and I know not a man." Joseph said "whence is that which is in thy womb?" Mary replied "As the Lord my God liveth, I know not whence it is come unto me."

Mary really did not know how she became pregnant. That lends more credence to the idea that she was put to sleep and artificially impregnated.

Joseph didn't know what to do. He thought to himself: "If I hide her sin, I shall be found fighting against the law of the Lord: and if I manifest her unto the children of Israel, I fear lest that which is in her be the seed of an angel, and I shall be delivering up innocent blood to the judgment of death."

So Joseph suspected that Mary's baby was an angel, an Elohim.

That night, an angel appeared to Joseph. The angel said to him: "Fear not this child, for that which is in her is of the Holy Ghost, and she shall bear a Son and thou shalt call his name Yahoshu, for he shall save his people from their sins."

This is important also. From the beginning, the angels knew the baby was a boy. They would only know this if an artificial means of conception was used, where they could determine the sex of the baby at conception.

I want to point out something else here. Again, many atheist and anti-Christian Web sites claim the virgin birth is not true. They say Joseph slept with Mary and is the father[61]. But the words of Mary, the words and reaction of the high priest, the reaction of Elizabeth, the words of Joseph, and the words of the angel all tell the story of a virgin birth. They were corroborated in three separate ancient texts: The *Infancy Gospel of James*, and the gospels of *Luke* and *Matthew*. Other writings in the Apocryphon agree but none say Joseph was the biological father. Matthew actually says, "Joseph did not know Mary till she brought forth her firstborn son." (*Matthew* 1:25)

Another claim is that the story of Jesus' virgin birth was copied from other ancient myths about virgin births, and, therefore, it is not true. Some of the other claims about virgin births were Krishna of the Hindus, Buddha from India, Mithra of the Persians, and Horus of the Egyptians. I took the time to investigate these stories. I don't think you want to read about them all now. I'll just summarize my conclusion:

1. In my opinion, none of them are as well corroborated and detailed as Mary's story.

2. Some of them include many wild claims, especially the story of Horus that tells about chopping up his father's body and putting it back together. Jesus' story does not have such wild claims.

3. It is possible, especially with Krishna and Buddha, that what happened to Jesus also happened with them. They were born from Elohim to save humans[62].

If you consider that Jesus traveled to the east to study the teachings of Krishna and Buddha, it fits together like pieces of a puzzle.

The last event I considered was the three wise men who visited Jesus after His birth. They were from Persia. Why would they care about the birth of a Hebrew unless they knew the baby was an Elohim? That may be why they came to see Jesus, bringing gold!

The Collection

At dinner, a soldier from the 101st Airborne was taking up a collection for new books for the new school they had built in Karbala. The books from the old school were filled with praises to Saddam Hussein, so the soldiers wanted to buy new ones for the children. I don't know why, but I gave fifty dollars. I'm not usually generous because I usually don't have extra money.

A package arrived for me after dinner. My sister, June, who is a CPA, sent it. It had a note in it. I don't have to file my income taxes until next year since I'm in Iraq—some presidential decree. It was April 15! I forgot all about taxes. She sent some pictures from Christmas and I started to get homesick again. I couldn't wait until July.

The next day there was another meeting for all nonmilitary personnel. The new interim Iraqi government was scheduled to take over on June 30, and the arraignment for Saddam Hussein would be shortly thereafter. They expected terrorist activity to increase to try and disrupt those events. We were warned again to be careful, stay in the work triangle, and stay with a buddy.

When I saw the collection guy from the 101st Airborne again after the meeting, I gave him another fifty dollars.

The Birth of Yahoshu IV

I read some more books of the Apocryphon. There were some amazing stories in it. I found out that the Apocryphon was included in the original King James Bible in AD 1611. So, Christians had been familiar with these writings until recent times.

I still wanted to find out more about Jesus being the seed of Eve who will crush the Serpent. I went back to my Bible to read the story of the Garden of Eden and the Serpent. It said that Eve ate the fruit from the Tree of Knowledge. Many times, the Bible talked about "knowing," and it meant sex and reproduction. (A man and a woman "knowing" each other.) In *Genesis* 4:1-3, Adam "knew" Eve and brought forth their child, Abel. The Bible said Joseph did not "know" Mary until she brought forth her first born son. (*Matthew* 1:25) In *Genesis* 4:17, the Bible says "Cain 'knew' his wife, and she conceived, and brought forth Henoch." Other examples of this could be listed. So I believe the Tree of Knowledge meant knowledge about sex and reproduction. For some reason, Adam and Eve could not have sex and reproduce.

In *Genesis* 2:21-23, God "cast a deep sleep upon Adam: and when he was fast asleep, he took one of his ribs, and filled up flesh for it. And the Lord God built the rib which He took from Adam into a woman: and brought her to Adam. And Adam said…she shall be called woman because she was taken out of man."

This may not mean God was creating a woman, like I was taught in Bible school. There were other places in the Bible where God had already created a woman.

Is it possible that something else was going on here? It had something to do with ribs. I looked up information on ribs on the Internet. I found cracked ribs, spare ribs, rib cages, ribbing, everything about ribs. And then, there was a link to DNA. It turns out that the ribs are the best place to obtain DNA. That gave me a theory[63].

The Serpent-guy in the Garden of Eden was probably an Elohim, and he was altering Eve to be able to reproduce by changing her DNA makeup. That's what was meant by "creating Eve," and "eating from the Tree of Knowledge." There were already women on Earth, but Eve would be able to have children. If the Serpent was an Elohim, he probably had the ability to alter DNA (remember Giza, the planets, the Sumerians, and so on).

This angered God, and those who had created man and woman. God did not want us to reproduce, calling human reproduction a sin. That was the *original sin*. Maybe, because of this, Adam and Eve were banished from the Garden of Eden[64].

That was also when they began to have children, after they were banished. So this made sense.

God then told the Serpent that Eve's seed (her descendants) will crush the Serpent's seed. Maybe that's why the Israelites conquered the Nephilim. I think the Nephilim were the Serpent's seed (descendants of Elohim, the sons of god, the angels).

I wasn't sure how Jesus would crush the Serpent's seed though. But maybe I had figured out what happened in the Garden of Eden.

Planet "X"

Well, once again, this was very different from the information I had been taught in Bible school. One night I tried to explain this to Lisa. I'm a masochist. She cut me off when I got to the part about artificial conception by stating that it wasn't artificial, it was immaculate, and the Serpent was the devil. She ended the conversation by saying that the Garden of Eden was mostly symbolic, like a fairytale, and we weren't supposed to pay too much attention to the details. We just need to know that we are basically sinners, and Jesus was sent to save us from our sins.

But are we basically sinners? I don't walk around committing sins. Lisa and Ricky are good people. Oh well, at least Lisa didn't laugh like a volcano.

I went into the museum early one morning before work to see Old One. He was sitting and polishing something. Old One looked very tired. I was kind of frightened by him, approaching slowly, timidly.

"Hello. Good morning. Can you talk to me now?"

Old One looked up. "Yes. You need to clear your mind." How did he know that? He began polishing again, in slow, circular motions.

I began to speak. "I'm kind of confused. Something happened in the Garden of Eden. I think that whoever created man and woman did not intend for them to reproduce."

I waited for a response. Old One looked up again.

"Yes. That is so."

I continued. "In the Garden of Eden, we were given that ability by the Serpent. It had something to do with DNA from Adam's rib. That was the fruit from the Tree of Knowledge, the ability to reproduce. I think the Serpent was an Elohim, one of the gods of Sumer." I waited for a response.

"Yes, go on."

"God was mad about what the Serpent did. He said the seed of the humans will crush the seed of the Serpent. Jesus and others have something to do with this. Jesus was the son of Yahweh. He was specifically bred for a special purpose. Mary really was a virgin." I was starting to ramble, so I stopped talking.

Old One looked very tired. "You need to clear your mind. Look to the sky. There is a visitor that enters the solar system from time to time, the most important times. It enters and leaves, and yet it is a part of our family. You need to discover this visitor." He stopped talking. I knew that it was time to leave.

"OK, but sir. I'm going home in July. I don't have much time. The Elohim, who--"

Old One waved his hand, cutting off my sentence. "The truth cannot come faster than it should. Then it would not be the truth to you."

He looked away. When he does that, it's like he goes into another world. I had to leave.

"Good day, um, sir." I turned and walked out of the museum.

Good day, um, sir? I always sounded like an idiot when I talked to Old One.

It was April 20. There was a ceremony on the base today. Some of the Marines were leaving, going home. They had finished their tour of duty. New Marines would replace them. A C-130 transport plane landed right on a small landing strip in the desert. I didn't realize how huge those things are.

Scoot was leaving. So was Ma'ad. I found them lined up with their gear, waiting to go. I hugged them both. They had been part of the invasion force from Kuwait. They had made it. They had survived! I was happy and sad. I will probably never see them again. Scoot said to tell Old One goodbye.

It's funny; I saw Old One having long conversations with some of the Marines and the Polish soldiers but with me, he only talks for a minute, and he makes me feel like an idiot. It's that Adam's rib thing. That story has been so misinterpreted. The Adam's rib story has been used for ages to prove women are inferior. Adam was created first, and then they used his rib to create Eve. So, woman was made from man. Man is superior. But none of that is true. Adam's rib was used to obtain DNA to give Eve the ability to have children. That's all. Old One did not dispute this. It is true.

Where the heck was I going to find out about this visitor to the solar system? It only comes at important times. It's part of our family. That sounds like a comet, maybe Haley's comet. Wait a minute—solar system, space, astronaut, NASA—Becky! The synapses in my brain connected. Becky would know this. She works for NASA. I'll send Becky another e-mail.

Becky, I have a riddle for you. There is a visitor that enters our solar system at the most important times. It enters and leaves, and yet it is part of our family. I need to discover this visitor. I need the answer as fast as you can. It sounded like a NASA question, so I asked you. Thanks and I have brown hair now. I'll be home in July. I'd love to see you. Maybe we can get together. Love, Joy.

I hate signing my name, "Love, Joy." It's like "Peace, Love, Joy." "Joy to the World." "Joy to One and All." Don't name your daughter Joy. I dated someone who would call me Joyous when he wanted to be cute. He didn't last too long.

Joy is one of those cute little names, like Eve, or Adam. Getting back to the story, something was bothering me about the Garden of Eden. According to the scientific evidence, the creation of Eve took place around two hundred thousand years ago. The Bible in *Genesis* and *Luke* only showed ten descendants from Adam down to Noah. I believe Noah's Flood was somewhere between 11,000 BC and 4000 BC. I've heard many different dates, but they've all fallen between that time period.

Our first ancestors would have had to live thousands of years if there were only ten descendants from Adam (approximately 200,000 BC) to Noah (between 11,000 BC and 4000 BC). Something was wrong here. Maybe not wrong, but I needed to figure this out.

I decided to look into this while I was waiting for Becky's answer. The first piece of information I came across was disturbing to me, to say the least. Most of the things I have discovered through Old One were disturbing. They contradicted thirty years of Church sermons, Bible school, and my religious beliefs. At times, I wanted to quit this and go back to the security of the Sunday sermons and what I was taught in Bible school. It's hard to change what has been programmed into my brain from day one of my existence. I kept thinking about the first thing Old One had said to me. *You may be worthy of the truth.* I think he may have meant that I would be able to accept this.

He also said the truth had to come in small amounts. That makes it easier to accept, to gradually break down the walls of thirty years of programming.

Anyway, I was willing to bet that the answer to my question about the descendants of Adam had something to do with the gods of Sumer. I decided to go to the Babylon bookstore to see what they had.

There were some books about Marduk, the god of Babylon. I wasn't sure if Marduk was one of the gods of Sumer, so I didn't look too long at those books. The Iraqi attendant tried to help me, glad to get a customer who wasn't a coalition soldier or an Iraqi policeman. He spoke very broken English. I told him I wanted information on the gods of Sumer. He said there were no books in English, but they were getting some. He was surprised when I told him I could read Arabic, telling me that I should read the "Enuma Elish." It was a Sumerian text. They didn't have it here, but he directed me to the reference computer in the corner of the store. He logged on and brought up a Web site[70]. This site gave a translation of the *Seven Tablets of Creation of the Enuma Elish*, by L.W. King, in English. These seven, sacred scrolls tell the story of creation.

They were shocking, at least to me, because each scroll corresponded to one "day" in the Torah and Bible stories of creation. For example, on day six in the Torah and Bible, God created man and woman. That corresponds to the sacred Sumerian scroll number six. On day five in the Torah and Bible, God said let the waters swarm with living creatures—the same as in sacred Sumerian scroll number five. On the seventh day in the Torah and Bible, God rested. That is the Sabbath day when we go to Church and praise God. On the seventh sacred Sumerian scroll, nothing was created. There were only praises to the god Marduk.

Each day of creation in the Torah and Bible corresponded to one sacred Sumerian scroll, in the same order. Now, I know the Bible story of creation was taken from the Torah. The question is: was the Torah taken from the seven sacred Sumerian Scrolls of the "Enuma Elish?"

I had to talk to Ricky. He was taught by Rabbis. He studied the Torah and would probably know the answer. I found Ricky sitting on *his* uncomfortable military cot, not really doing anything, just staring. I was very wound up and didn't say hi or make small talk. I just started right into it.

"Ricky, I have a very serious question to ask you. I always thought that Moses wrote the first five books of the Bible, the Torah. I thought that God dictated them to Moses on Mt. Sinai. That's what I was taught in Bible School." I suddenly remembered Ricky's *Reader's Digest* version of the Babylonian captivity. "It just dawned on me that a while ago, you said the Torah was partially written in Babylon. Is that correct?"

"Yes, when the Hebrews were captured by Nebuchadnezzar," he answered pensively.

"Did they take *Genesis* from the Sumerians, from something called the 'Enuma Elish,' the seven sacred scrolls?" I was talking a mile-a-minute.

Ricky had that uncomfortable look again. "Maybe." He paused. I didn't think he was going to say anything else. Then he began again, in a slow and defensive tone of voice. "I know they got a lot of…information from the Babylonians, who got a lot of their information from the Sumerians."

I started twirling my hair, my subconscious way of trying to make Ricky talk faster.

"The Hebrew priests were very impressed with the Babylonian mystics and their knowledge. They, I guess you could say, copied a lot of their beliefs from them."

"But, did they copy the creation story from them?" I was still talking fast.

Ricky again answered slowly. "Well, some scholars say they did."

"Ricky, did you know that each one day of creation in the Torah and Bible corresponds to one of the seven sacred scrolls in the same order?" I began again, like a machine gun. "Like, on day five in the Torah and Bible, it says God created all of the creatures that crawl. It also says the same thing on the sacred scroll number five from the 'Enuma Elish.'"

"I think I heard something about that one time. I didn't think too much about it," Ricky replied deliberately.

I began speaking fast again. I think I ate too much sugar that day. "But, do you realize that there are debates and arguments that have taken place for centuries about the days of creation? Some Christians believe that because the Bible used the word 'day,' the whole universe was created in seven twenty-four-hour periods. Those who believe in the Big Bang theory argue that the Universe began with an explosion about fifteen billion years ago and the 'day' in the Bible means some eon of time, like millions or billions of years. But one 'day' really means one sacred Sumerian scroll of the 'Enuma Elish!' Neither group was right. *One 'day' means one scroll!*"

Ricky wasn't as impressed with all of that as I was. Maybe the reason was because he's Jewish, and therefore hadn't heard the fierce debates some Christians have had about the word "day" in the Bible. Or maybe I was talking too fast. I sounded like Alvin the Chipmunk. Also, Ricky seemed to be familiar with the "Enuma Elish." It's almost as if he was trying to keep it a secret. The whole conversation was disappointing.

Since Ricky wasn't impressed with my great discovery, I decided to go back to finding out why the anthropological record shows that Adam and Eve lived two hundred thousand years ago, but only ten descendants in the Bible separated them from the time of Noah's Flood. Noah's Flood was somewhere between 11,000 BC and 4000 BC. I played around on the Internet, trying to find clues about that.

While I was playing around, I came across something else that was interesting. On a Web site by Daniel Ward, there was a story about the life of Adam. Remember when I said God and someone else made man and woman somewhere, and then put Adam only into the Garden of Eden to work? Well, I came across the tale of Lilith. Evidently, Lilith was the daughter of one of the gods of Sumer. When Adam was brought to Eden to work, Lilith was supposed to be his consort. She refused because Adam was not a god. So, after some period of time, a human woman was brought to Eden to become Adam's companion—Eve[71].

Here's another story that agrees with the idea that Eve was not created from Adam's rib!

I couldn't find anything on the Internet that explained the ten descendants from Adam to Noah. I decided to go back to the Babylon bookstore. I wanted to ask the Iraqi salesperson about the descendants of Adam and Eve. He seemed to be very knowledgeable. I tend to underestimate the Iraqis. They are an ancient and intelligent people. When I asked my question, he knew what I was talking about, giving me a bound manuscript called the *Sumerian King's List*. He said it would explain everything, and of course I was too embarrassed not to purchase this one. When I asked what the price was, the Iraqi attendant said " Only fifty American dollars." Never underestimate the Iraqis.

The book described clay tablets written in cuneiform, the writing language of the Sumerians, which give a list of the Kings of Sumer before Noah's flood. These clay tablets were found in Iraq by archaeologists and sent to libraries around the world. On some lists, there were ten kings; on others, eight kings. One list began over two hundred thousand years ago, another over three hundred thousand years ago, and others started over four hundred thousand years ago. According to this manuscript, the kings were the descendants of Adam listed in the Bible. The clay tablets were saying these kings, descendants of Adam, each reigned for thousands of years. If that's true, then the first descendants of Adam each lived for thousands of years[72]. This is going to seem unbelievable, but please keep reading. It's what our ancient ancestors wrote down for us. They were trying to tell us something.

Just to make it more confusing, the Sumerian names on each list were somewhat different from each other. Also, the Sumerian names were different than the Bible names of Adam and his descendants. Here is the list that made the most sense to me. This tablet is kept in the National Library of Norway:

King Number	Sumerian Name	Bible Name	Years of Reign Before Flood
1	Alulim/Adapa	Adam	222,600-193,800
2	Elalgar	Seth	193,800-150,600
3	Ammilu'anna	Enos/ Cainan	150,600-114,600
4	Enmegalanna	Malaleel	114,600-85,800
5	Dumuzi	Jared	85,800-57,000
6	En-sipa-zi-anna	Enoch	57,000-43,200
7	Meduranki	Methusale/ Lamech	43,200-36,000
8	Ubur-Tutu	Noah	36,000-Flood

The manuscript also said the kings ruled from five different Sumerian cities, changing periodically. The names were Eridu, Bad Tibira, Larak, Sippar, and Shuruppak. The fact that the cities are named made this a little more believable. But it was still pretty bizarre. The first seven or nine descendants of Adam were kings, and they each lived and ruled for thousands of years. I don't know whether or not I can believe this.

In my Bible, in *Genesis,* it lists Adam and his first nine descendants, and how long they each lived. Adam lived for 930 years, Seth lived for 912 years, Enos for 905 years, and so on. I always had a hard time believing they lived for hundreds of years. Thousands of years seemed impossible.

The manuscript I purchased addressed the difference in the king's list and the Bible. It said the Sumerian number system was based on the number sixty. They had a symbol of sixty that resembled the number one. The early writers of the Torah used the symbol for sixty as the number one[73].

So, each age listed in the Torah and Bible for Adam's first descendants should be multiplied by sixty. That would make the ages listed in *Genesis* look like this:

Name	Bible Age	Actual Age
Adam	930 yrs x 60	55,800 yrs
Seth	912 yrs x 60	54,720 yrs
Enos	905 yrs x 60	54,300 yrs
Cainan	910 yrs x 60	54,600 yrs
Malaleel	896 yrs x 60	53,700 yrs
Jared	962 yrs x 60	57,720 yrs
Enoch	365 yrs x 60	21,900 yrs
Methusale	969 yrs x 60	58,140 yrs
Lamech	777 yrs x 60	46,620 yrs
Noah	Not Given	Not Given

Each of the first ten descendants from Adam to Noah lived for tens of thousands of years, and they each ruled as a king in Sumer for some portion of their life—thousands of years.

I know—this is too unbelievable! However, just suppose this is true. The *Sumerian King's List* kept in the Library of Norway fits with the anthropological and DNA evidence, which shows that Eve was created around two hundred thousand years ago. The ages in the Bible, if multiplied by sixty, also show that the descendants of Adam and Eve could fit into the *Sumerian King's List*. So—maybe it could be true?

I decided to keep this information to myself. I could not possibly show this to Ricky and Lisa. There is no way they would believe this. But the cuneiform tablets—they can't all be made up stories. There must be something to this. The *Sumerian King's List* fits the creation of Eve evidence. It also fits the Bible list if we believe the Torah writers used the Sumerian symbol for sixty as the number one.

I still have to keep this to myself. No one will believe this...except, maybe, Old One. He was starting to give me the creeps. I began imagining he was really hundreds of years old, maybe thousands. OK, Joy, back to reality. Get ahold of yourself. I decided to keep this *Sumerian King's List* in my own memory bank, in my own cerebral cortex.

The Beheading

It was the end of April, and I was watching the news one evening with Ricky and Lisa. The terrorists had captured an American contractor and were holding him. They threatened to cut his head off unless the United States withdrew its troops from Iraq. I didn't think he had much hope of being released because he was American and Jewish. Every night, for at least a week, the news stations showed pictures of the contractor, blindfolded, with masked terrorists standing behind him. Then, finally, the deadline for removing our troops passed. The terrorists coldly, horribly beheaded him. He was alive and screaming while they used a knife to saw through his neck. There were five of them, with hoods over their heads. They shouted "Allahu Akbar"—"God is the greatest"—the whole time they sawed through his neck. They videotaped the beheading with sound and posted it on the Internet.

"Allahu Akbar"—"God is the greatest." These people had no idea what they were doing. They cut another human being's head off to prove God is the greatest?

What killed me was that very few news people commented on how horrible, evil, and demented these terrorists were. Instead, most of them focused on whether we should be in Iraq or not.

That was very frustrating to someone who was in Iraq.

Planet "X" II

Becky's e-mail didn't help to improve my mood either.

Hi, Joy. I can't answer your question. I think I know the answer, but if I told you I'd be in BIG trouble. This is classified NASA information. We're under congressional order not to divulge classified NASA information. Who gave you this riddle?

I'll give you a hint, though. It's not a comet. I know you are smart enough to find this yourself.

It's been a very hot spring here. That sun is relentless. I thought about going to Mars to get some relief, but I heard they're having a heat wave there, too. You know how fast I turn red.

Call me when you get home.

Love, Becky

What the heck was she talking about? Mars, the sun, classified information, turning red? Maybe she was working too hard. She didn't make any sense. Becky was having one of her goofy periods. She had those in college. She would be silly and unfocused for a couple of days. Everything was a joke to her. Then she would snap out of it and become Becky the genius again. It was her way to recharge herself. Did she have to do it now when I needed her?

I went to sleep thinking Becky wasn't going to be any help. However, my brain kept thinking about this while I slept. When I woke up, I understood what she was doing. It wasn't a goofy period. She was trying to tell me the answer. It had something to do with the sun being very hot, Mars having a heat wave, and the color red. I couldn't wait to get finished with work so I could investigate this.

I found a lot of information on my computer by beginning with

NASA, Mars, and then the sun. I became so engrossed in this that I stayed awake all night. Here's a list of the information I found:

1. NASA classifies information about anything that may be a cause for alarm among the general public. They have to give this information to Congress and the White House but cannot release this to the rest of us. So if NASA discovers that a comet will hit our planet next week, or an alien race is headed toward Earth to vaporize all of us, they have to keep it a secret and only tell Congress and the White House. We are doomed! I won't make any more jokes about Congress right now[74].

Anyway, the answer to Old One's riddle must be a cause for alarm among the general public (that's us) because it is classified.

2. Becky said they were having a heat wave on Mars. That's true! Cal Tech planetary scientists believe the polar ice cap on Mars is melting. Dozens of deep, wide pits in the southern ice cap have been growing larger every year. They believe this is caused by global warming on Mars. Someone must be driving SUVs on Mars. The Cal Tech scientists have theorized that if both Mars and Earth are experiencing global warming, then the source is somewhere out in the solar system[75].

(So. It's not caused by SUVs. That's good news because I may plan on being a soccer mom and driving an SUV someday. If I ever find Mr. Right.)

3. The sun is going crazy. The sun is more active now than it has been for a millennium. There have been more sunspots per year from 1940 to 2004 than for the past 1,150 years. A sunspot is the result of fierce magnetic activity inside of the sun. Sunspots make giant plumes of material burst out from the sun's surface. Some of this material travels to Earth. The information about sunspots comes from two sources—observation of the sun back to the seventeenth century when the telescope was invented, and from testing ancient ice cores in Greenland and Antarctica for beryllium-10. This is kind of complicated. Beryllium-10 is always in the atmosphere. It comes from outer space. But, when the sun is active, its magnetic field shields the earth from beryllium-10. The testing of the ice cores on Greenland and Antarctica found that levels of beryllium-10 are scarcer now than they have been for a very long time because the sun has become more active[76]. And that means some major portion of the earth's global warming may be due to the sun's activity. The sun's activity is also causing global warming on Mars!

A Finnish research team calculated the average number of sunspots per year back to AD 850:

SUNSPOTS PER YEAR	YEARS
30	AD 850-1900
60	AD 1900-1944
76	AD 1944-Now

Also, the sun is supposed to go through eleven-year cycles of maximum and minimum activity. The last maximum cycle was supposed to have ended in 2001. On October 13, 2003, sunspot number 486 appeared, and it was the biggest one in thirteen years. This is supposed to be a period of minimum activity. The sunspot activity will lessen, but we will have a shortened minimum period[77,78].

Some scientists have concluded that the sun has begun to interact with something heading toward our solar system. The interaction is causing the excitement on the sun's surface. I found a theory of what the sun is interacting with in *Genesis Revisited*, by Zecharia Sitchin. I had finally purchased that book from the Babylon bookstore.

1. A strange gravitational force acting on Uranus, Neptune, and Pluto is pulling down on the planets, instead of making them wobble from side to side. Whatever is pulling them is below instead of on the orbital plane of the other planets.

2. According to Sitchin, *The Washington Post* ran a story in 1983 which reported that NASA's Infrared Astronomical Satellite detected heat from an object about fifty billion miles away. The article said it was a "heavenly body possibly as large as Jupiter, and possibly so close to Earth as to be part of this solar system." *U.S. News & World Report* carried a similar article in 1984. In 1987, NASA research scientist John Anderson was quoted in *Newsweek* as saying that an "eccentric tenth planet may or may not be orbiting the sun." He called this Planet X in the article[79].

It's curious that this story seemed to die in the 1990s. I found little about it dated in the 1990s, after a lot of information dated in the 1980s. In my opinion, that's when it became classified.

Anyway, there is a good chance that a Planet X is beyond Pluto in a different orbital plane than the other planets. It must have an elliptical orbit, because it is heading toward the sun right now. Planet X must be fairly large because the sun has begun interacting with it. That is what's causing the sunspots!

It all made sense. That's what Becky was trying to tell me. There is another planet beyond Pluto with an extreme elliptical orbit. It goes away from the sun for awhile, and then turns and heads toward the sun. It must have just recently turned back toward the sun in the last century or two, causing an increase in sunspots. The question is: how close does it get to the sun and the Earth? And when will it get here?

I remembered the riddle. Old One said it comes at important times. I began thinking. What were the most important times in history? I thought about the World Wars, Columbus' journey to America, the Black Plague, the Crusades, the Barbarian invasions of Rome, the Mongol invasions of China, and many other things. I asked Ricky and Lisa at work for their opinions. They added Moses leading the Hebrews out of Egypt, the founding of Israel in 1948, the creation of the United Nations, the founding of the United States, the Russian Revolution, and many others. Then Lisa, who is sometimes a genius without knowing it, said "Noah's Flood."

All of our brains hit their brakes and stopped thinking. Of course, Noah's Flood. That may be the most important thing that happened to the Earth. Noah's Flood! And could it be that Planet X caused the flood with its gravitational pull as it headed toward the sun? I hugged Lisa, and of course she thought I was crazy[80].

I started thinking again. When was Noah's Flood? I've heard anywhere between 11,000 BC to 4000 BC. It couldn't have been around 4000 BC when the Sumerian civilization began. And that's another most important event. The first civilization—Sumer! So that's two: Noah's Flood and Sumer. The flood could not have happened too close to the beginning of Sumer. I would imagine that the waters would have taken centuries to recede, and it would have taken thousands of years to repopulate the earth.

I remembered from my anthropology course in college that something called the Neolithic Period began around 7500 BC. This was when the first villages appeared, along with the first domesticated plants and animals, and the beginning of pottery making and weaving. The oldest known village, Jericho, in Israel, was founded at this time. The Neolithic culture developed in the Tigris and Euphrates River Valleys in Iraq, and spread to the Nile River Valley in Egypt, the Indus River Valley in India, and the Huang He River Valley in China. (I got an "A" in anthropology.) This would be the third most important time. So, Noah's Flood would have to be prior to this. By the process of elimination, it must have occurred around 11,000 BC[81].

OK. What else happened that was important? Then it hit me—The birth of Jesus, Yahoshu!

Noah's Flood	11,000 BC
Neolithic Culture	7500 BC
Sumer	4000 BC
Birth of Jesus	0

Those were the most important times! Could they be the dates that Planet X has passed by? If that's true, then Planet X has a very long orbital period, about three to four thousand years. If it takes that long to go once around the sun, it would mean Planet X has just completed about half of its orbit and is on its way back. So, if all of this is true, it won't pass by the Earth and the sun until sometime in the fourth millennium AD. According to Zecharia Sitchin in *Genesis Revisited*, the orbit takes 3,600 years.

After I figured all that out, I found a Web site with the same information. It even had a calculation of how long Planet X is visible in the sky as it passes by us about every three thousand years. The calculation was based on Kepler's mathematical laws. This is for mathematics geeks, but is interesting. The years in this chart are total, coming and going. The chart also showed how fast Planet X would travel[82]:

LOCATION	YEARS	SPEED
Outermost boundary of Pluto	59.35	22,000 mph
Within orbit of Uranus	15.22	22,000 mph
Within orbit of Saturn	5.80	27,000 mph
Within orbit of Jupiter	2.64	55,000 mph
Within asteroid belt	1.90	65,000 mph

For some reason, the chart did not give the time from Mars to the sun and back again. My guess, based on the above chart, would be ten years. We cannot see beyond Saturn with the naked eye. So, Planet X would be visible in the sky for only about twenty years. However, if you had a decent telescope, you may be able to see it for thirty years or longer. NASA would certainly know about it for at least hundreds of years in advance.

I also ran across information about something called *The Kolbrin*, an ancient manuscript that talked about Planet X. The authenticity of the manuscript is being debated, but it called Planet X "The Destroyer." *The Kolbrin* said "The Destroyer" returns periodically and causes destruction on earth. "The Destroyer" was responsible for Noah's Flood, and the appearance is described as fiery and red[83]. If that is true, then Planet X has an internal source of heat. The red color of Planet X was what Becky was trying to tell me in the e-mail! She said that she gets red fast. Thank you again, Becky.

Well, I guessed I had the answer for Old One. I wondered why he wanted me to find out about Planet X? We went from the birth of Jesus to outer space.

Reincarnation and Resurrection I

The next day, I found some time to see Old One. He was writing something furiously. Once again, I felt a little afraid to approach him. He didn't look up, even though he knew I was there.

"Hello, Sir. Is this a good time to talk to you?"

"Yes." He stopped writing.

I began my explanation. "The answer to your riddle, um, there is a tenth planet in the solar system. This planet takes between three and four thousand years to orbit the sun, has a very elliptical orbit going way out into space, and passes close to the sun[84]. It is not on the same orbital plane as the other planets, possibly coming from below them. When it passes by the Earth, it can cause great destruction, such as Noah's Flood. Other important times it passed by the Earth include the start of the Neolithic Period, the beginning of Sumer, and the birth of Jesus." I finished, feeling very proud of myself.

All Old One said was, "It was not a riddle."

He always did this. Now I felt stupid again. We stood there, not talking, just looking at each other. I had to say something.

"Um, why did you want me to find out about this planet? What does it have to do with Jesus and God?"

"It is essential for the truth." Old One looked around the room. "Who knows about this…planet?"

"Um, do you mean, well, um," I stammered, much to my disgust. "I think, well NASA." I suddenly remembered from my research that the Sumerians knew about Planet X! "Oh, and the Sumerians did, too. They called it, um, Nib, Nib, uh, Nibonic. Or something like that."

Old One shook his head. Then he spoke again. "I want you to find out about something that will make you feel better. All of the ancient peoples believed in the same thing."

He seemed sad. Looking down at his paper, he started writing again. It was time to leave. *Nib, Nib, Nib, uh, Nibonic.* Ugh! I went back to my uncomfortable military cot and looked up the information I had about Sumer. The Sumerians called Planet X "Nibiru," not Nibonic. I had said Nibonic, how embarrassing.

I knew the answer to this new question as soon as Old One had asked it. What did all of the ancient peoples believe in? I wanted to say it then, but I was too embarrassed because I stuttered so badly about Nibiru. The answer is reincarnation. Almost all of the ancient peoples had some form of reincarnation as part of their belief system. Here are the ones popping into my brain:

1. Buddhists (China, Tibet, Southeast Asia)
2. Hindus (India)
3. Taoists (China)
4. Celtics (Northern Europe)
5. Incas (South America)
6. Mayans (Mexico)
7. Gallics (France)
8. Manichaeans (Iran)
9. Followers of Plato (Greece)
10. Gnostic Christians (North Africa)
11. North American Indians (U.S. and Canada)
12. Inuit (Arctic Circle and Greenland)
13. Old Egyptians (Egypt)

I think I just covered the whole ancient world. Also, the followers of Pythagoras made reincarnation one of their main beliefs[85].

You remember the Pythagorean Theorem from geometry class, don't you? Two sides of a right triangle squared always equal the hypotenuse squared. 'A' squared plus 'B' squared equals 'C' squared. (No wonder I'm not married yet.) Anyway, Pythagoras had a cult following in ancient Greece, and they believed in reincarnation.

A lot of famous people have believed in reincarnation, like Benjamin Franklin. Here's the epitaph Benjamin Franklin wrote for his tombstone:

The body of Benjamin Franklin, printer, like the cover of an old book, its contents torn out and stripped of its lettering and gilding, lies here, food for worms. But the work shall not be lost; for it will, as he believed, appear once more in a new and more elegant edition, revised and corrected by the Author[86].

He was talking about his own death and rebirth.

Some other famous people who believed in reincarnation were Madame Curie, Mark Twain, General George Patton, Walt Whitman, Henry Ford, Elizabeth Browning, Edgar Cayce, and so on[87].

Today, billions of people believe once you die your soul comes back in another body—reincarnated. However, billions of others don't believe in reincarnation. Officially, Christians do not, although I saw an article which claimed that, according to the Harris Interactive Poll, twenty-five percent of Christians believe in reincarnation[88].

I remembered the story of Elijah and John the Baptist. Those who believe it have to acknowledge the possibility of reincarnation.

A prophet named Malachi, living around 500 BC, made a prediction, recorded in the Old Testament, about signs to look for before the Messiah was born. "Behold, I will send you Elijah, the prophet, before the great and dreadful day of the Lord." (*Malachi* 4:5) Elijah was a prophet who lived around 800 BC. He was supposed to come back right before the Messiah.

In the New Testament, Jesus twice says that John the Baptist is a reincarnation of Elijah:

For all the prophets and the law have prophesized until John. And if you are willing to receive it, he is the Elijah who was to come. (*Matthew* 11:13-14)

And later:

And the disciples asked him saying 'Why then do the scribes say that Elijah must come first?' But he answered, 'Elijah has come already, and they did not know him, but did to him whatever they wished. So, also shall the Son of Man suffer at their hand.' Then the disciples understood that he had spoken of John the Baptist. (*Matthew* 17:10-13)

When John the Baptist was asked if he was a reincarnation of Elijah, he said "I am not." So what is the truth here? It could be that they were both telling the truth as they knew it. Those who believe in reincarnation say people usually do not remember their past lives. So John would not know he had been Elijah. He was not lying. John the Baptist wore camel hair clothes and had a wild and unkempt appearance, just like Elijah. His diet consisted of locusts and honey, just like Elijah's. He came out of the desert, preaching, like Elijah. He preached that the day of the Lord was at hand, just as Malachi had predicted. Maybe Jesus was telling the truth[89].

Whenever I explain this to a Christian, they just look at me with a blank expression. It's not important to them, which is curious. But if it's true, this is one case of reincarnation!

Fatima

We hired an Iraqi woman who had been in exile in London for eight years before the fall of Saddam Hussein to work at the power station. Once she had learned of his capture, she came back with her family. I asked her what her name was.

"Oh, I am named after Mohammed's daughter. Blessings of Allah be upon them." She replied. Then she didn't say what the name was. She just assumed I would know it!

"I'm sorry. I don't know the name of Mohammed's daughter. What was her name?"

She looked at me as if I was from Planet X! "You do not know the name of Mohammed's daughter?"

"No, I'm sorry, but I don't."

I guess that came as quite a shock to her. She was quiet for a few seconds.

"Fatima," she said finally. "Mohammed wrote that Fatima was the most blessed of all women in Paradise, after Mary. Fatima said she surpasses all women, except Mary. That is who I am named after." She threw her head back in a defiant gesture[90].

OK, fine. Her name is Fatima, the most blessed of all women in Paradise, except for Mary.

"My name is Joy. Nice to meet you." It would have been funny if my name was Mary. We shook hands. Fatima smiled.

"You bring joy to this life?"

That was a good question.

"I try to!"

Well, we had an awkward beginning. I hoped it could only get better.

Fatima wore a headscarf and a long tunic-like dress. It wasn't drab black like many of the women here wear but was off-white with gold decorations on the fringes—quite pretty. She had long, dark brown hair, and light brown eyes.

Later, when I told Lisa about our meeting, she told me a story about the town of Fatima, in Portugal. That is the town where Mary, the mother of Jesus, is supposed to have appeared in 1917, and was also named after Mohammed's daughter. I never knew that.

The Moslems from North Africa had occupied Portugal for many centuries. After a long series of wars, they were driven out. The last Moslem ruler had a beautiful daughter he had named Fatima, after Mohammed's daughter. Right before he left, she fell in love with a Catholic prince from the town. Fatima stayed behind and married the prince. The prince loved her so much he renamed the town Fatima. Lisa said that it's interesting Mary picked this town to appear in. The Moslems revere Mary and passionately defend the idea that she was a virgin. So, Mary picked a town with the same name as the daughter of Mohammed. Since then, Mary has been known as "Our Lady of Fatima[91]."

I know there is something significant to that, but right now it's beyond my brain. I'm still working on reincarnation.

I asked Fatima if Moslems believe in reincarnation. She started quoting from the Quran to me. She called it the "noble Quran."

"Here is what Allah almighty said in the noble Quran: 'From the earth did we create you, and into it shall we return you, and from it shall we bring you out once again.'" (*Quran* 20:55)

Fatima said it means we will resurrect, not reincarnate.

OK, Moslems do not believe in reincarnation. I noticed in the quote from the Quran there was that "we" thing again. "We" create; "we" return. Allah had help creating and returning. That was just like God in *Genesis*, who had help creating man!

Reincarnation and Resurrection II

I had the answer for Old One: reincarnation. Almost all of the ancient cultures believed in reincarnation. But I didn't want to talk to Old One yet. I wanted to find out two more things: did the Sumerians believe in reincarnation, and why do official Christian and Moslem dogmas not include it? I started with the Sumerians. Remember when Old One asked what the riddle of Sumer was? One of the discoveries I made was that the Sumerians worshipped a lot of gods. They had a plethora of gods. I like that word, "plethora." It reminds me of one of my favorite movies, *The Three Amigos*. The bad guy in the movie, whose name was "El Guapo," had a "plethora" of piñatas for his fortieth birthday. Oh God, I'm thirty years old, heading toward forty! But if I'm going to reincarnate, then maybe I shouldn't worry about it.

Anyway, one of the Sumerian gods was named Enki. The Sumerians believed he created the first humans. I decided to see if there was any connection between Enki and reincarnation. I was playing around on Web sites, looking for Enki, and came across something called "Adapa's Treatise." It said that for Enki to create a human, a god had to be slaughtered. The god's blood would be mixed in clay with something from a hominid to create a human[92]. That's how Enki created us! A ghost would come into existence from the god's flesh. The ghost would remain. They informed the god while he was still alive of his "token." The ghost was interpreted to mean a soul. The text said this was done on the first, seventh, and fifteenth of the month. So, the Sumerians believed that humans were given the souls of gods. The soul would continue on, just as in reincarnation.

All right, the Sumerians had their own weird version of reincarnation, but they believed in it too! So why didn't the Christians and Moslems?

I thought it would be a good idea to talk to the Catholic priest who visits the base on Sundays. The following Sunday I caught him at the entrance to the church tent before Mass began.

"Hello, Father. Um, my name is Joy. I work for the power company here on the base."

He stuck out his hand to shake mine. "Everyone calls me Father Mike. How are things going for you here?"

"Oh, good. OK."

"Well, it's an honor to meet you." Father Mike said, smiling.

Honor to meet me? Father Mike was young and very good looking. Very good-looking men should not be priests. BECAUSE THEY CAN'T GET MARRIED.

I began a little slowly. "If you don't mind, I have a question for you."

He smiled again, nodding for me to continue. He had an air of happiness, or more like satisfaction about him, making me feel comfortable.

"I've been doing research for a project about ancient religions. It seems like almost every religion believed in reincarnation except for the most recent ones, Christianity and Islam. Do you have any explanation for that?"

"Hmm." Father Mike's forehead wrinkled. "How much do you know about the idea of reincarnation?"

"Uh, I know some things." I sounded like an idiot.

"Did you ever read anything by a man named Ian Stevenson?" Father Mike asked, and then continued without waiting for my answer. "This man spent his entire life researching reincarnation. He worked at the University of Virginia, but he traveled around the world investigating claims of reincarnation. I read his book, *Twenty Cases Suggestive of Reincarnation*, in which he practically proves that it does happen."

"So, Father, you believe in reincarnation?"

"Joy, I didn't say I believe in it. It's something to consider though."

I wanted to get him to admit he believed in it. I went right to my ace in the hole!

"What about John the Baptist? If he wasn't Elijah reincarnated, then Jesus wasn't the Messiah."

"I think that if he wasn't Elijah, it would just mean the Elijah prophecy was not fulfilled," Father Mike responded quickly. "Joy, maybe we

120

should talk about the early Christian Church. How much do you know about church history?"

"Uh, I know some things." I couldn't believe I said that again!

Father Mike pushed his hair back from his forehead, making him even more good looking. "After the Ascension of Jesus, Christians split into two groups, Gnostic and Orthodox. A lot of what the Gnostics believed was lost until the discovery of their scrolls in 1945 in Upper Egypt. They had fled to Egypt when the Romans invaded Jerusalem in AD 70. I have read about these scrolls. It seemed to me that a lot of what they tell resembled descriptions of what we know from near death experiences, even stating that we will encounter a divine light after death. They explored what happens after death a lot deeper than the Orthodox Christians[93]."

A soldier walked past and pointed to his watch.

"Oh, sorry, Joy. I should get ready for Mass now. Can I talk with you after?"

"Yes, please. That would be great, Father. I want to hear the whole story."

Father Mike began putting on his vestments, and so I took a seat in the church tent.

The Mass

I hadn't been to a service for a few weeks. It felt good to be in a church, or at least a church tent. I looked around. It was crowded. A lot of the soldiers are religious. My dad always said, "There are no atheists in foxholes."

The service topic made me feel uneasy. Father Mike began by reading a passage from the *Books of Kings* about King Solomon. King Solomon! Solomon worshipped Astarte, the goddess.

Then Father Mike talked about the Lord God Yahweh, and how Yahweh gave wisdom to Solomon. I think Yahweh was an Elohim, maybe one of the gods of Súmer. *Yahweh may have killed tens of thousands of people!* He destroyed Sodom and Gomorrah and wiped out the Nephilim.

Father Mike continued on with the Mass and then gave a sermon. He talked about Jesus dying on the cross to save us from our sins, and stated that it is our nature to be sinful as a result of the events in the Garden of Eden, when Adam and Eve disobeyed God by eating the fruit of the forbidden tree. That was the first sin, our original sin.

The forbidden tree was the Tree of Knowledge, about sex and reproduction. Jesus wasn't saving us from that. I started thinking. I believe a lot of the Old Testament has been misinterpreted: most of *Genesis,* the creation story, the story of Adam and Eve, the stories about Yahweh, and probably Noah's Flood. The events leading to the birth of Jesus have not been written fully in the New Testament. The authors leave out most of the information about Jesus' youth. In my opinion, His messages to us and reason for dying on the cross have been distorted. He didn't die on the cross because Adam and Eve ate fruit from a tree!

The Mass

The Mass ended and I was still thinking. I felt relief, like I always do when the Mass ends. I believe that goes back to when I was a child and my mother took me to Masses that were in Russian. I didn't understand a word the priest was saying, and they lasted almost two hours. When they ended, I always felt relief.

Reincarnation and Resurrection III

After the Mass, I stood in front waiting for Father Mike, trying to get into a more congenial mood.

Father Mike walked over to me. "Hello Joy. I have a few minutes now."

"Thank you, Father."

"Let's sit down over here, Joy."

We sat on the edge of the little stage used as an altar during the Mass. Father Mike began the conversation again.

"I think we were talking about the Gnostics and the Orthodox Christians. The Gnostic Christians had a very spiritual approach to God. The Orthodox approach was more worldly and ritualistic. The Gospel of John begins with a Gnostic saying: 'In the beginning was the Word, and the Word was within God, and the Word was God.' (*John* 1:1)

"The Word is the part of God that acts in the world. It is the union between God and us. The Word is the divine spark that is in everyone. We are all a part of God."

So that's what it meant. I always wondered about that.

"We existed before we were born. Every human is an incarnation of the Word. We all have the potential to be a Christ, and every soul will be drawn back to God."

The words were mesmerizing. Father Mike's voice was so peaceful and calm that I felt as if I was in a trance. Snap out of it, Joy.

"Um, Father Mike, that sounds beautiful, peaceful." Then it dawned on me. "That sounds like reincarnation!"

"Yes, it does," Father Mike agreed. "That's why the book of *John* was almost rejected when the New Testament Canon was put together. Pre-existence of the soul and reincarnation were not accepted."

We were silent for a moment, and then my mind lurched into action.

"But…I guess that's my question. Why not?"

"In my opinion," Father Mike began again, "a lot had to do with the Gnostic Christians being very secretive. They claimed to possess secret knowledge about the meaning of the resurrection. This secret knowledge was restricted to people who qualified to be initiated and receive the secret teachings. This is in contrast to the very term *catholic*, which means 'universal.' 'Catholic' implies that anyone could become a member of the Church. Most of all, the Gnostics emphasized spiritual resurrection instead of physical resurrection. Spiritual resurrection is, of course, reincarnation."

"Spiritual resurrection, reincarnation, as opposed to everyone coming out of their graves at the end of the world." I clarified.

Father Mike's eyes brightened. "Yes. That's it. You get the idea."

I felt like Eliza Dolittle from *My Fair Lady. I think I've got it!* I tried to repeat it. "So the Orthodox Christians based their religion on the second coming of Jesus. And the Gnostic Christians based their religion on reincarnation."

Father Mike shook his head "no." I guess I'm not Eliza Dolittle.

"Well, I wouldn't put it that way. They both based their beliefs on the teachings of Jesus. What happened was that the Gnostics made a lot of enemies among their fellow Christians, claiming Jesus performed secret initiation rituals and revealed a secret teaching to those who were capable of receiving it. The secret teaching was only given to a few, unwritten by the apostles. To those on the 'outside,' everything was said in parables so they would be ever seeing, but never perceiving. You can see how this would cause resentment among those on the 'outside.' As the followers of Jesus increased and became more organized, those on the 'outside' began to suppress the Gnostics. Eventually, all who denied or questioned the resurrections at the second coming of Jesus were considered heretics. The Gnostic doctrines were gradually edited out of the official Church doctrines. As the Church became more entwined with the Roman government, it even began to persecute those who followed Gnosticism. They succeeded in wiping out Gnosticism, and with it, reincarnation[94,95]."

"So that's what happened to reincarnation in Christianity!" Now I've got it.

Father Mike smiled, nodding. "An early church leader named Origen said 'The soul has neither beginning nor end…They come into this world strengthened by the victories or weakened by the defeats of their previous lives[96].' Origen was eventually condemned as a heretic."

"Father," I had to ask again, "you *do* believe in reincarnation, don't you?"

He didn't answer me, just shrugging his shoulders and smiling.

"Joy, I hope to see you next week at Mass."

I wondered if the New Testament had any sayings of Jesus about reincarnation. I walked back to my uncomfortable military cot and opened my Orthodox Bible. Of course, there was John the Baptist. Jesus said that John was the reincarnation of the prophet Elijah.

Here is a conversation about reincarnation Jesus had with His apostles in *Matthew* 16:13-14: "When Jesus came into the coasts of Cesarea Philippi he asked his disciples saying, 'whom do you say that I the Son of Man am?' And they said, 'some say that thou art John the Baptist, some Elias, others Jeremias, or one of the prophets.'"

The disciples were saying people believed Jesus was a reincarnation of one of the prophets. Or, some people believed the spirit of John the Baptist, who was dead by this time, had possessed Him. Jesus replied that He was an incarnation of God, but He did not dispute the possibility of reincarnation or of spirit possession!

In *Revelation* 3:12, John quotes Jesus as saying: "Him that overcometh will I make a pillar in the temple of my God, and he shall go out no more." That sounds like reincarnation! If you overcome evil or sin, you can stay with God and you will not have to "go out." You will not have to reincarnate (come back in a body) again.

In *John* 9:1, the disciples showed their belief in reincarnation. One day they walked past a man who was blind from birth. The disciples asked Jesus: "Rabbi, who has sinned, this man or his parents, that he should be born blind?" The disciples thought maybe the man had done something wrong in his past life, or maybe his parents had, and he was paying for it in this life with his blindness. That is also the law of Karma, which is part of the doctrine of reincarnation! And once again, Jesus' answer did not deny the possibility of reincarnation.

A famous saying of Jesus is that you will reap what you sow. This is paraphrased from a parable in *Matthew* 25:14-29 and *Luke* 19:11-26. It means if you do something good, then something good will happen to you. The law of Karma.

Jesus also said that to enter the Kingdom of God, "you must be born again." (*John* 3:7) Did Jesus mean reincarnated? He continued, saying, "The wind blows where it will, and thou hearest its sound but dost not know where it comes from or where it goes. So is everyone who is born of the Spirit." (*John* 3:8) That sounds like Jesus was trying to explain reincarnation.

Other quotes in the Bible may allude to reincarnation. I don't want to overdo it here, so I'll stop.

I completed more research and found out that the Christian Church Council of AD 553 in Constantinople officially tried to put an end to the doctrine of reincarnation. They rejected all of the Gnostic Gospels, which had references to reincarnation, and wrote "anathema's" condemning Origen and the idea of pre-existence of the soul[99].

One of the Gnostic Gospels was the *Gospel of Thomas*. Number 84 in this Gospel quotes Jesus as saying "when you see your likeness, you are happy, but when you see your images that came into being before you and that neither die nor become visible, how much will you have to bear?" Once again, this sounds like reincarnation[97].

In another Gnostic Gospel called *Pistas Sophia*, Jesus is quoted as saying, "Souls are poured from one into another of different kinds of bodies of the world." Reincarnation? These were rejected from the official Church Canon.

Flavius Josephus, the Roman/Jewish historian, is quoted as saying "All pure and holy spirits live on in heavenly places and in course of time, they are again sent down to inhabit righteous bodies[98]."

OK, I'll *really* stop now.

I didn't consider reincarnation too much before this. I thought it would be nice if it was true, but it didn't seem possible. Thirty years of being taught resurrection makes it hard to believe reincarnation. But if Jesus talked about it…maybe. If most of the ancient cultures believed it…maybe. Maybe it is true.

Now, what about the Moslems? Why don't they believe in reincarnation? Fatima! I'll ask Fatima tomorrow.

Oh, one other thing. I also read that a lot of the beliefs of Orthodox Christianity came from St. Paul. He had been a Pharisee before he became a follower of Jesus. The Pharisees believed in strict ritual observation and—resurrection.

Fatima Again

I wanted to approach this subject carefully with Fatima. Moslems seem to be more sensitive about questioning their beliefs than Christians or Jews. You can be the judge of how careful I was.

"Fatima, I wanted to ask you something about religion. It's just something I'm curious about. Do you mind?"

"No, I like to talk about religion and Allah," Fatima replied.

"Well, it's not actually about Allah," I continued cautiously. "It's about what I asked you the other day."

Fatima thought for a second. "That was…reincarnation?

"Yes!" I exclaimed, impressed that she remembered.

"OK. What is the something you want to ask me about reincarnation?"

"Well, the thing is, Fatima, I was doing some research. Almost every ancient culture believed in reincarnation. Today, Hindus and Buddhists believe in it. Some Christians do too."

"Those were all religions that were not perfected." Fatima interrupted.

That took me by surprise. "Uh, um, what do you mean by 'they were not perfected'?"

"Joy, don't you know that is why the angel Gabriel gave the Quran to the Prophet Mohammed? Peace and blessings of Allah be upon him."

All I could say was "What?" Did she peace and blessings on—whom?

Fatima kept going. "That is why no prophet can come after the holy prophet Mohammed. Peace and blessings of Allah be upon him."

This wasn't going too well.

"Fatima, I was asking why Moslems and the majority of Christians don't believe in reincarnation when it seems like everyone else does, or did."

"But Joy, I am explaining that to you. Islam is the final perfection of all religions. When Allah perfected the religion, he taught humanity two things. On the one hand, he taught humanity the lesson of unity; on the other hand, he declared finality of prophethood. This was for the reason that all worship of one God should be under the banner of one religion."

I tried to get back to the subject of reincarnation. "OK, but I don't see what that has to do with reincarnation."

Fatima was getting impatient. "I am getting to that. You see, we have the saying 'La ilaha illallah.' There is no God but Allah. Hazrat Isa, peace and blessings of Allah be upon Him, was a great prophet, but He was not the last."

"Fatima, I'm sorry, but I don't know what the heck you are talking about! Who is Hazrat Isa?"

"He is Jesus!" Her voice was getting higher.

"Oh, OK Fatima, but what does all that have to do with reincarnation?"

"When Allah perfected the religion and gave the holy Quran to the holy prophet Mohammed, peace and blessings of Allah be upon him, it said that we will resurrect, not reincarnate. Reincarnation is not in the Quran. Therefore it cannot be true," she answered in her high voice.

I think she was angry. Her hand was waving in the air.

"So, it is not in the Quran?" I asked.

Fatima was still talking in a high voice, and now her index finger was pointing in the air.

"The noble Quran says this: 'We shall not die, except our first death.' (*Quran* 37:58) That means we will only die once. That is what is says in the Quran. That is what is true[100]!"

Fatima was pretty passionate. Her voice was an octave higher than usual. I could see I wasn't getting anywhere. I will have to figure this out for myself.

Fatima did have flawless logic though. The Quran perfected the writings of all other religions. Reincarnation was not in the Quran. Therefore it cannot be true!

Reincarnation and Resurrection IV

Mohammed received the Quran around AD 600. That was only about fifty years after the Council at Constantinople. The Council declared reincarnation to be heresy and resurrection to be the correct dogma. The Quran continued the dogma of resurrection.

Gabriel (the angel, Elohim, whatever) dictated the Quran to Mohammed. Gabriel left out reincarnation and talked about resurrection.

OK, Fatima said the purpose of the new religion, Islam, which Gabriel gave to Mohammed, was to unify all humans under the banner of one religion. The word "Islam" means submission, submission to Allah. Gabriel wanted us to be unified under one religion and one God, Allah. Not Yahweh!

So what was going on here? The only conclusion I could make was that it would be easier to unify everyone and have them submit to Allah with the dogma of resurrection. If everyone has to worry about the day they will be resurrected and judged, they will submit to Allah's wishes. If everyone thought they were going to reincarnate, they may not be so submissive. It's almost like a conspiracy. We were deliberately steered away from believing in reincarnation by Gabriel and the Council of Constantinople.

There is one more interesting item I should write about. I did some research on Ian Stevenson, the person Father Mike talked about. A great deal of his research was conducted in the country of Lebanon, among a group of people called the Druze, or Druse. The Druze follow the practices of the Shiite Moslems, with a big exception. They believe in reincarnation. About nine hundred thousand Druze live in Lebanon. They claim that one way someone will remember their past life is if they die young and in a violent way, because in those cases, the soul was not ready to leave and clings to the memory of its past body.

After the Lebanese Civil War in the 1980s, cases were documented by Ian Stevenson of Druze children remembering a past life in which they were killed violently. Some of the deaths they remembered were from the Lebanese Civil War[101].

I mentioned this to Fatima.

"The Druze are not Moslems," she said, "they are Druze. In fact, they are descendants of the Crusaders."

With Fatima, everything was black and white, no gray areas.

Well, I was ready to talk to Old One. I found him in the museum writing again. I wondered what he was writing about. He seemed to be engrossed in it. Just as before, I felt nervous about approaching him. I coughed and made clomping noises with my feet as I walked to get his attention. I sounded like a horse, but he still didn't look up. I decided to talk anyway.

"Hello again, sir."

He continued to write as he talked. "Now do you believe that Yahweh and Allah are still fighting today?"

I didn't expect that question.

"Uh, well, um, I guess so. The followers of Yahweh are the Jews and the Christians. The followers of Allah are the Moslems. They are fighting in some places. I guess some Moslems want to conquer the Jews in Israel."

Old One stopped writing. "Yes."

I kept talking. "Allah requires complete submission and a one-world religion. Yahweh said there should be no other gods before Him. So they are still fighting. Or I mean their followers are. But I thought you were asking me about reincarnation."

"Yes." Old One nodded. "That is what I asked you about. It will make you feel better when you find out the truth."

Good topic. I wanted to ask about the truth.

"Um, sir, about that truth, I'm leaving in three weeks--"

"You will be told the truth." Old One cut off my sentence. "You must do one more thing. Learn the resurrection and ascension of Jesus."

Well, I figured Old One believed in reincarnation. He probably assumed I did now also. Wait. If Old One believed in reincarnation, then he couldn't be a Moslem. I wondered if he was a Druze?

Learn the resurrection and ascension of Jesus. One last thing!

The Spanish

The Spanish contingent left Camp Babylon.
It was eerie.
They left after dark in a convoy.
They were going to the Baghdad airport to board airplanes for Spain.
The Spanish just sneaked out of here.
There was no ceremony, no television, and no news coverage.
We all felt a little uneasy about the pullout.
It was a victory for the terrorists.

Resurrection and Ascension of Jesus I

I had three weeks to study the resurrection and ascension of Jesus. Then, finally, I would be told whatever it was that Old One considers the truth. Maybe I should only take two weeks. What if I had to leave early or I couldn't find Old One when it was time to leave?

At this point, I was very unsure about what I believed. My brain had this new information stored in memory:

1. Jesus' mother, Mary, and grandmother, Anna, may have been impregnated by angels, Yahweh, or whoever the Elohim are.

2. Mary was impregnated in a way that she still remained a virgin.

3. It appears that Jesus believed in reincarnation, or at least He didn't dispute it. Father Mike thinks it may happen. He read Ian Stevenson's scientific research on the subject.

4. Allah, or Gabriel, did not want us to believe in reincarnation. Neither did the Christian Church leaders at the Council of Constantinople. That is why it is not in the Quran, and there is little about it in the Bible. Resurrection at the end of the world is believed instead.

5. Elijah may have reincarnated as John the Baptist.

6. Planet X is heading toward the sun. It will get here after the year AD 3000. It may have caused Noah's Flood. Planet X has something to do with Jesus and the Truth.

This information is in addition to gold, Nephilim, no missing link, Giza, and everything else. Before I met Old One, I would never have believed any of this. But now I thought it was all very possible. Back at the beginning, I said what happened to me here in Babylon, Iraq is something you should know about so you would be able to make up your own mind.

But to know this, you should go through the same process I did. It is almost finished, so please persevere and bear with me.

I know the resurrection of Jesus is a very controversial subject. There are those who say the resurrection of Jesus is the foundation of Christianity. If you don't believe Jesus physically rose from the dead after His crucifixion, you cannot be a Christian. It is more fundamental than the virgin birth or any other idea in Christianity. Personally, I have always accepted it, but, secretly, I have longed for some type of proof. I've heard all of the theories about what else may have happened instead of a resurrection, such as what Fatima told me:

"They did not kill Hazrat Isa, they killed a likeness of Him that was shown to them. It says that in the holy Quran. Allah would not allow such a great prophet to be killed by infidels."

The exact quote from the Quran is: "yet they did not slay him, neither crucified him, only a likeness of what was shown to them." (*Quran* 4:156) The Moslems believe that someone who looked like Jesus was substituted for Him on the cross[102].

Those who don't believe have many other explanations:

1. Jesus did not die on the cross. He was still alive when He was put in the tomb, where He regained consciousness and walked out.

2. His body was stolen by the apostles, who then fabricated the resurrection story.

3. Jesus' appearances after the crucifixion were only visions. He did not have a physical body.

Those are the main theories, along with Fatima's explanation[103].

During the course of my research here in Babylon, I have come to believe that there is always some truth to ancient texts, no matter how bizarre they may seem. Many ancient texts mention the resurrection of Jesus. Many talk about the resurrection as an accepted fact. For example, I came across two letters written by Ignatius (AD 50-115), a follower of Jesus and an early church leader. He compiled letters to the Trallians and the Smyrnaeans, where he wrote in an almost matter-of-fact way about the resurrection. Another example is a letter by Pope Clement I around AD 96. He talked about the resurrection in a letter to the Corinthians.

Flavius Josephus, the Roman-Jewish historian, is reputed to have written in AD 93 that Jesus "appeared alive again the third day as the divine prophets had foretold." The authenticity of this writing is in dispute. Other Christian leaders around the same time wrote letters about the resurrection. Some of these were Polycarp, Justin Martyr, and Tertullian. And, of course, we have *Matthew, Mark, Luke,* and *John* in the New Testament. The Romans, Hebrews, and others killed people who spoke or wrote about the resurrection of Jesus. Eleven of the twelve apostles were murdered for teaching about Jesus and the resurrection! So, if these writers and speakers did not believe Jesus resurrected, I don't think they would have put their lives in danger by saying that He did.

The question is *why* did they believe such an implausible story?

As with almost everything else, my search led me to Sumer. All roads may lead to Rome, but everything else leads to Sumer.

I discovered some pretty amazing information about the Sumerians. Evidently, the Sumerians had advanced medical knowledge. In 3000 BC, they did not have Shamans or healers. They had physicians. I need to explain what their physicians could do in order to make a point about resurrection in Sumer. Here are some facts about Sumerian physicians:

1. Skeletons in Sumerian graves bore unmistakable marks of brain surgery.

2. A partially broken Sumerian medical text speaks of the "surgical removal of a shadow covering a man's eye." This may mean a cataract.

3. Another medical text speaks of the use of a cutting instrument and states "if the sickness reached inside the bone, you shall scrape and remove."

4. Other texts deal with diagnoses and prescriptions.

5. The Sumerians had mineral solvents, mineral baths, and rubbing compounds.

6. They had medicines made from plants, and liquid and powder applications.

7. Some texts spoke about alchemy, cloning, and even DNA knowledge.

8. Alcohol was used as a disinfectant.

9. Medical schools taught anatomy and dissection of animals. They had knowledge of the human organs[104].

I know all of that information is hard to believe about a civilization that existed in 3500 BC. But that is what their ancient texts say. And it gets more interesting. In their texts are references to efforts to resurrect the dead, especially if the dead were the gods of Sumer.

There is a story about the goddess Inanna. The goddess was killed during a dispute with her sister. The following is from a Sumerian text about her revival, or resurrection.

"Upon the corpse, hung from the pole, they directed the pulse and the radiance. Sixty times the water of life, sixty times…the food of life, they sprinkled upon it and Inanna arose."

The goddess Inanna died and was resurrected!

The Sumerian texts go on to describe the attempted resurrection of Inanna's lover, Tammuz. The resurrection did not work, and Tammuz remained dead. It's interesting that at least up until the time of the prophet Elijah, Hebrew women of Jerusalem had an annual day of lamentation for Tammuz[105]!

I'm sure if I discussed these stories with Ricky or Lisa, they would tell me they were just myths. But if we believe all of the other information about Sumerian physicians, why would only the resurrection stories be a myth?

From Egypt, there is a story in the *Pyramid Texts* of the resurrection of a god named Horus. Horus was stung by a scorpion when he was a child and died. His goddess mother, Isis, called upon the god Toth, who came down from heaven and resurrected Horus.

The Sumerians and Egyptians believed these resurrections had taken place. The Hebrew women of Jerusalem must have believed it also.

What really surprised me were two passages in the *Books of Kings* in my Orthodox Bible that described resurrections:

> And it came to pass after these things, that the son of the woman, mistress of the house, fell sick; as his sickness was so sore, that there was no breath left in him…And the Lord heard the voice of Elijah; and the soul of the child came into him again, and he revived. (1 *Kings* 17:17, 22-23)

That's one resurrection. Here is the second:

> And it came to pass, as they were burying a man, that, behold, they spied a band of men; and they cast the man into the sepulchre of Elisha; and when the man was let down, and touched the bones of Elisha, he revived, and stood up on his feet. (2 *Kings* 13:21)

This man was already being buried, and he was resurrected. Since the *Books of Kings* were in the Old Testament, I decided to discuss them with

Ricky. I wondered, if he doesn't believe that Jesus resurrected, does he believe the resurrection passages in the *Books of Kings*?

Once again, I found Ricky sitting on his uncomfortable military cot, just staring. Something was troubling him. He reminded me of Old One, lost in his thoughts.

The Elliot family picture was hung on the wall by his cot. Ricky was an only child. He was in the front of the picture. Behind him was Mr. Elliot, dressed Orthodox style in a black coat and top hat. Mrs. Elliot was strikingly beautiful, with dark, curly hair.

Next to the family portrait was a college picture. Ricky had a beard, and he was holding a sign that said "FU–Florida University." He had left out the word "State"–typical Ricky Elliot. I asked my question with typical Joy bluntness.

"Joy," Ricky responded, aggravation in his voice, "I believe the Hebrew Scriptures, and I never said Jesus did not resurrect." He hesitated, like he usually does. When he hesitates, he usually looks in my eyes to try and read my expression.

"You know, some Jewish people suspect that…" he hesitated again, "…that Jesus was the Messiah. What we do not accept is Christianity."

We were both silent for a minute.

"Well Ricky, if you think Jesus may be the Messiah, then why wouldn't you accept Christianity?"

"Because Christianity does not follow the laws of God."

That was a surprise. The part about not following the laws of God was a discussion for another day. Ricky believes that resurrections took place in the Old Testament and that Jesus may have resurrected!

The Urantia Book

Jesus Himself was involved in the resurrection of Lazarus. I found the story of Lazarus in an *extremely* unusual place. At work, someone had left *The Urantia Book* [116] next to a circuit hub I needed to test. I had heard of this book. I think it's one of those New Age writings, and Urantia followers believe we have made contact with beings from another star system, the Pleiades. They believe Jesus was one of the beings from that star system. I laughed to myself as I paged through it. How can people believe these things? Who the heck was reading this book? It was in English. I suspected it was Ricky! He seemed to be searching for something, and when you are searching, you will look everywhere.

As I looked through the book, I was surprised to find out that the Urantia Foundation has been around since 1955. That's almost twenty years before I was born. For some reason, I didn't think people had ideas like that back then.

I was even more surprised when I came to "Part IV: The Life and Teachings of Jesus," and then "Paper 168: The Resurrection of Lazarus." I didn't expect to see these things in *The Urantia Book*. I began to read.

According to *The Urantia Book*, Lazarus' sisters, Martha and Mary, sent word to Jesus that Lazarus was desperately ill. While the messenger was on the way to Jesus, Lazarus died. The only response from Jesus was, "This sickness is really not to the death." Martha and Mary did not understand this response. Lazarus died, and after three days he was placed in a tomb. On the fourth day, Jesus arrived at the tomb. The women said, "If only you had been here, my brother would not have died!" Jesus replied,

"Your brother will rise again." Martha answered, "I know that he will rise again in the resurrection of the last day."

This conversation showed the Hebrew belief in resurrection on the last Day of Judgment, just like the Christians and Moslems.

Jesus asked for the tomb to be opened. Martha and Mary objected. According to *The Urantia Book*, the Hebrews believed that the soul stays around the body for three days after a person dies. On the fourth day it leaves and that is why the body begins to decay on the fourth day. Martha and Mary believed it was too late. *The Urantia Book* also said resurrection at this point (four days) requires "a far greater organization of universe facilities." The book did not explain what that means.

Next, Jesus prayed to His Father and then said "Lazarus, come forth." Lazarus was bound in grave clothes and his face was covered with a napkin. He sat up on the edge of the stone shelf where he had been laying and walked out. All who had witnessed this, except the apostles, fled. They were overcome with astonishment and fear. *The Urantia Book* went on to talk about how the former adjuster of Lazarus had to resume abode in the mind and soul of the resurrected man. The book didn't explain what that meant either.

According to *The Urantia Book*, many people came to believe in Jesus because of the resurrection of Lazarus. But, His enemies became more fearful. At one o'clock the next day, the Sanhedrin (the Hebrew ruling council) met to deliberate the question "What shall we do with Jesus?"

A certain Pharisee presented a resolution calling for his immediate death, proclaiming that he was a menace to all Israel. The Sanhedrin feared serious complications with the Roman authorities would arise, since so many of His followers regarded Jesus as the Messiah, Israel's deliverer. Caiaphus, the high priest, said "It is better that one man dies, than the community perish."

So, according to *The Urantia Book*, the resurrection of Lazarus set the stage for the crucifixion of Jesus!

When I explored the story of Lazarus on the Internet, I ran into a few anti-Christian Web sites that claimed the story was not true, asserting that it was copied from an Egyptian tale about Horus. Evidently, there was an Egyptian story that Horus' father, Osiris, had been chopped into pieces. He was put back together by Horus and brought back to life. Another name for Osiris was Asur, and he was also called El-Asur. The Web sites stated that the name El-Asur became Lazarus in the Bible. So they claimed that the story of Jesus and Lazarus was copied from Horus and El-Asur. The story of Jesus and Lazarus, therefore, was not true.

These anti-Christian Web sites were beginning to get on my nerves. That Horus/El-Asur/Lazarus idea really seems like a stretch to me.

The resurrection of Lazarus is also told in the New Testament in *John* 11:1-44. It says just about the same thing as *The Urantia Book*. However, *John* does not mention anything about forces of the universe or adjusters of the mind and soul.

The main point for me was that the followers of *The Urantia Book* believe Jesus caused Lazarus to resurrect. The writers of the Bible, the Sanhedrin, and the Pharisees believed it. Many witnessed this and became followers of Jesus or fled. They all accepted that Lazarus was resurrected. Because they knew resurrection had happened before?

Resurrection and Ascension of Jesus II

Let's go back over the cases of resurrection:

1. The goddess Inanna of Sumer was resurrected by using the pulse and the radiance, and other items.

2. Her lover Tammuz died, and a resurrection attempt failed.

3. Horus, the Egyptian god, died from a scorpion bite. He was resurrected by Toth, who came down from heaven.

4. In the *Books of Kings*, Elijah resurrected a boy.

5. In the *Books of Kings*, a man was resurrected when he "touched the bones of Elisha."

6. Lazarus was resurrected by Jesus. We don't know how. In the New Testament book of *John*, the author does not tell what happened in the tomb. *The Urantia Book* has its own theory of how Lazarus was resurrected.

These resurrections had one thing in common: someone else resurrected the dead person. They did not resurrect themselves.

With that in mind, I wanted to compare the resurrection of Jesus to the other resurrections. I spent another evening on my computer and with my Orthodox Bible. I found the story of Jesus' resurrection recorded in the books of *Matthew, Mark, Luke, John, Acts of the Apostles*, and *Letters to the Corinthians*. While some of the accounts appeared to be contradictory, others reconciled the differences. Here is a summarization of the "harmonized" accounts:

Jesus died on the cross on a Friday. Two men, Joseph of Arimethea and Nicodemus, immediately took Jesus' body down from the cross. Joseph of Arimethea was not mentioned in connection with Jesus prior to this. So this is a mysterious development. Jesus was put in a tomb owned by Joseph of Arimethea.

On Sunday, Mary Magdalene, Mary the mother of James, Salome, Joanna, and at least one other woman left before sunrise for the tomb. They carried spices to anoint Jesus' body.

They reached the tomb after sunrise and saw that the stone blocking the entrance had been rolled away. Mary Magdalene looked inside the tomb and saw that it was empty.

Mary Magdalene ran to get the apostles Peter and John, who were still in Jerusalem. The other apostles had fled to Bethany.

The other women then entered the tomb and saw two "angels" sitting there. Evidently, Mary Magdalene had not seen them. The women were frightened of the "angels," and they bowed down to the ground. I found this curious. Why were they so frightened of the "angels" that they had to bow down to the ground?

The "angels" said, "Why do you look for the living among the dead? Do not be afraid, for I know that you are looking for Jesus, who was crucified. He is not here; He has risen, just as He said."

For the next forty days, Jesus was seen at different places[106,107].

Some of the accounts, but not all of them, tell of an earthquake at the tomb, the "angels" appearing, and the "angels" blinding and scaring away the Roman guards. That reminds me of the angels blinding the townspeople of Sodom.

I wondered exactly what these "angels" were.

Jesus' burial garments were found in the tomb in the same position as when he lay in them. Peter assumed this meant Jesus resurrected Himself[108]. And this is where I have a different theory. In every recorded resurrection case I had found—the Sumerians, the Egyptians, Lazarus, and the others—someone else was involved. The dead persons did not resurrect themselves. In the case of Horus, the text was very specific that the god Toth caused the resurrection. The god Toth was an Elohim.

Inanna, the goddess from Sumer, was an Elohim. The angels in the story of Sodom and Gomorrah were Elohim. Angels were in the tomb of Jesus.

Here is my theory: the Elohim knew how to resurrect a dead person in the first few days after death. It didn't always work. Inanna could not resurrect Tammuz. But it worked for Inanna, Horus, and Jesus. The angels resurrected Jesus. Also, I think Joseph of Arimethea was connected with the

Elohim. That is why Jesus was put in Joseph's tomb immediately after He died! That is my theory, based on what I have read about the Elohim, resurrection, and the story of Jesus. The angels (the Elohim) resurrected Jesus.

To me, this makes the most sense. I don't believe the other theories, and here is why:

1. Jesus was not alive when He was put into the tomb. He had been scourged with a whip, had a crown of thorns pressed into His head, carried a cross, was nailed to a cross, hung on a cross for hours, and had a spear puncture His heart. He couldn't have lived through that.

2. The apostles could not have overpowered the Roman guards and stolen the body. The Gospels say that most of the apostles had fled from Jerusalem to Bethany in fear for their lives.

3. Jesus' spirit was not appearing everywhere instead of His body. That wouldn't explain what happened to the body in the tomb. Also, in His appearances, people touched Him and He ate food. That isn't what spirits do.

4. Someone was not substituted for Jesus on the cross. As far as I can tell, that story did not surface until six centuries later when Mohammed obtained the Quran. The Quran is the only writing I have found that claimed a substitution. All the Gospels and letters of the years immediately after Jesus' time say it was Jesus who died on the cross. So do any references found among Roman records, including Josephus. Also, in the six hundred years before Muhammad, many thousands were martyred for believing Jesus died on the cross and was resurrected.

5. It was not possible for Jesus to resurrect Himself. The angels in the tomb had to do it. All of the other resurrections I found information on were carried out by another person—not by the dead person.

So, I believe that Jesus was resurrected by the angels, the Elohim. The resurrection story is true, but just like the virgin birth, the Elohim were responsible for it.

The New Government and Heaven

The new government of Iraq was supposed to take over on June 30, 2004. A formal ceremony was going to be held in the Green Zone in Baghdad. The Coalition president, Paul Bremer, would officially hand over control of the Iraqi government to the new Iraqi Council and to the new Iraqi president, Dr. Iyad Alawi. Everyone here at Camp Babylon was prepared to watch the ceremony on that date. It was a big step forward, only a little more than a year after the invasion. Elections by the people of Iraq were scheduled for early in 2005. However, the Coalition leaders surprised everyone, including the terrorists. The ceremony actually took place two days earlier on June 28[117].

We were allowed to go to the dining area to watch the ceremony. I sat with Ricky, Lisa, and Fatima. The Iraqi government officials all mentioned Allah in their speeches. Fatima pointed that out. Lisa mentioned that George Bush ends a lot of his speeches with "God Bless America," to which Ricky responded that European leaders are not allowed to mention God in their speeches. Fatima agreed. When she was living in London, the only leaders talking about God were Moslem leaders. That's interesting. The Church of England has become silent.

The ceremony became a little boring and we were distracted. The conversation changed to a discussion about heaven when I mentioned that Old One told me to study the resurrection and ascension of Jesus. Right now, I told them, I'm trying to find information about the ascension of Jesus into heaven. Fatima made a surprising comment.

"I do not like to speak about heaven."

"Fatima, did you say you don't like to speak about heaven?"

"Yes, that is what I said," she repeated emphatically.

"Well, why wouldn't you like to talk about heaven?"

She looked at me intently. "Because for women, I do not think it will be such a..." she paused, looking for the right word, "a satisfied place for women."

I began to feel like a prosecuting attorney, pressing on with the questions. "You mean, heaven is different for men and women?"

We were all staring at Fatima, waiting for an answer. She wanted to say something but held it in, mumbling something, and then stopped talking. I didn't let her off of the hook. My lawyer instincts had taken over.

"What did you say?"

"Joy, it is too embarrassing to talk about. I don't think the prophet Mohammed, peace and blessings of Allah be upon him, would be happy with me."

I wouldn't let her out of the witness chair. "Why? What's wrong?"

Ricky intervened; the judge yelling at the attorney for badgering the witness. "Joy, don't push it. She doesn't want to talk about it."

Hmm...I think Ricky is still aggravated with me from our discussion about resurrections. I turned to Judge Ricky.

"OK. Fine. I won't push it." Maybe it's a good thing that I'm leaving Iraq. Tempers have been short lately.

"No, it is OK." Fatima spoke again. "I can say something."

"See, it's OK." I stuck my tongue out at Ricky. Then I felt like I was five years old. Fatima broke into a brief smile at this, before becoming serious again.

"It seems like in heaven, the main purpose of women will be to service men's desires."

We were all silent, just staring at Fatima.

"The worst part is, for each man, we will have to compete with seventy-two virgins."

"Sounds more like hell than heaven!" I blurted out without thinking. I was sorry after I said that, coming across as if I was making fun of Fatima's beliefs. That's against one of my rules. Never make fun of someone's religious beliefs. "Oops! I'm sorry, Fatima. That surprised me. You mean each man gets seventy-two virgins in heaven?"

"Yes, seventy-two virgins, if they are martyrs. Right now, there are a lot of martyrs. I would be one of the virgins in Paradise."

"But, you could only do that one time, right?" I continued with the

150

cross-examination. Fatima looked very puzzled. She didn't answer. "I mean, you can only be a virgin one time, right?"

"No, you can be a virgin more than once. These things can be true in Paradise." Fatima said with resignation, sighing. We all looked confused. She continued. "For men, there are eight heavens. They are different, how do you say, steps of happiness. Each heaven has many pleasures. But, in the holy Quran, it teaches that the greatest pleasure is seeing Allah face to face[120]."

We were all quiet for a minute, letting what Fatima said sink into our brains. Lisa finally broke the silence.

"Jesus said his Father's house has many mansions. Maybe that means the same thing. There are different degrees of happiness in heaven."

Judge Ricky shuffled his feet and cleared his throat. Mr. "Aggravated With Me" was going to speak!

"Does anyone have an idea of where heaven is?"

Lisa jumped right on this question. "I think it's in some other dimension. Did you know when the Big Bang happened, there were eleven dimensions created in the first second? We can only perceive four dimensions: length, width, height, and time. But, there are eleven. I learned that in quantum physics."

She was beaming. We all stared at Lisa like we had stared at Fatima.

"Oh, and the universe can split to make other universes that are not accessible to our own." We kept staring at her. "What? You don't believe me? There are particles that do not interact. Neutrinos pass through the earth, millions per second, right through to the other side without interacting."

It was like Lisa had been waiting for a year to say all that.

"So, you think heaven is in another dimension?" I asked.

Lisa said "Yes!" with passion[118,119].

Ricky coughed again. He looked as if he was going to make a great announcement. "Did anyone ever read Psalm 75?"

We were all silent, now staring at Ricky.

"I thought so. It says, 'When I shall receive the congregation I will judge uprightly…For promotion cometh neither from the east, nor from the west, nor from the south.' That tells you where heaven is."

We still stared blankly at Ricky. How does that tell us where heaven is?

"That means heaven is not in the east, west, or south," he continued, "So, it must be in the north. From anywhere on earth, north is only one way—up." We were still staring. "Don't you get it? Elijah was taken 'up' into heaven. The heavens opened 'up' to Ezekial, and a whirlwind came out of the 'north.' Jesus was taken 'up' into heaven. Job was talking about heaven. He said God stretched out the 'north' over the empty space. Heaven is up!"

I had to ask. "Up where?"

"Up there, in the sky, in the universe." Ricky was getting excited.

"That is what I thought. Heaven is beyond the stars," Fatima said.

Lisa gave her opinion. "Beyond the stars could be another dimension."

"No, it is a real place." Ricky was aggravated again. "That's what I've been trying to tell you. People went there. Elijah, Enoch, Jesus[110,120].

I decided to be a wise guy. "OK, if that's true, how long does it take to get there?" I didn't expect Ricky to have an answer. Ricky had an answer.

"Right around the time of Jesus, a respected teacher, Rabbi Gamliel, said the exact spot in the heavens where God has a dwelling is so far that it would take a journey of about 3,500 years to get there[109]."

Well, everyone stared at Ricky again. No one had expected an answer to that question. Attorney Joy returned.

"How did Rabbi Gamliel know this?" I asked.

"I don't know. Maybe God told him," Ricky shot back.

Ricky was definitely aggravated again. I thought this was ridiculous. Ricky believes that it takes about 3,500 years to journey to heaven because some rabbi said it two thousand years ago!

The ceremony ended and we went back to work but I kept thinking about Rabbi Gamliel and 3,500 years. For some reason, that number seemed familiar to me. Why was that so familiar? Then the answer began creeping into the back of my brain. The flood. The Neolithic Period. Sumer. The Birth of Jesus. They were each about 3,500 years apart. What happened every 3,500 years? Planet X came here. It takes about 3,500 years for Planet X to orbit the sun.

Something else bubbled up in my cranium. Eight levels of heaven! Fatima said there were eight levels of heaven. I think I know what they are:

1. The Moon
2. Mars
3. Jupiter
4. Saturn
5. Uranus
6. Neptune

7. Pluto
8. Planet X

Planet X is heaven, or I think it's what the ancient peoples called heaven. That is where Elijah and Enoch went, where the Elohim and Jesus went.

Christians say the highest level of heaven is seventh heaven. The Christians do not count the moon. There are seven heavens if you don't count the moon. The Moslems must have counted the moon because Allah was originally the moon god. When the ancient peoples spoke about going to heaven, they meant Planet X.

There must be life on Planet X!

The ancient texts were not talking about where your soul goes when you die. When the ancient texts talked about heaven, they meant Planet X, a real place. Ricky was correct.

Resurrection and Ascension of Jesus III

I began to suspect the Elohim were from Planet X. Old One said learning about Planet X was essential for the truth. The Elohim must be from Planet X. That would explain everything. Anyway, I still had one more task—the Ascension.

I went back to the Internet to find out about the Ascension of Jesus. I had to hurry—only a few days were left until I would leave Babylon.

First of all, Ricky was correct again. There were other ascensions to heaven. As with everything else, the first ascension was in Sumer. A person named Adapa was given a "shem" by Enki (the Elohim) to take him to heaven. A "shem" is a Sumerian word that could mean "a ship that flies," like a space ship. Adapa went to heaven in the shem, received important knowledge, and then returned to Earth in the shem[114].

The next person who ascended to heaven was Enoch. He was one of the first descendants of Adam and number seven on the Sumerian King's List. Enoch went to heaven twice. "And Enoch walked with God after he had begotten Methuselah three hundred years, and begot sons and daughters, and all the days of Enoch were 365 years, for Enoch walked with God and was gone, for God had taken him. (*Genesis* 5:21-25)

The Torah says Enoch walked with the "Elohim," not God. In the *Book of Jubilees* it states that Enoch went with the angels of God, and they showed him everything which is on Earth and in the heavens.

Fragments of a text called the *Book of Enoch* say the angels swiftly lifted Enoch and carried him off "to the highest heaven." In my opinion, the highest heaven is Planet X!

In another ascension recorded in *2 Kings* 2:2-5, Elijah, the prophet, went to heaven. First, Elijah was told to go to Beth-El by the Lord. His disciples asked one of Elijah's assistants if the prophet was going to be taken up to the heavens. The assistant answered "the Lord will take away the master today." Then "there appeared a chariot of fire, and Elijah went up into Heaven by a whirlwind." (*2 Kings* 2:11)

There was also the story in the Biblical book of *Ezekial* about the king of the city of Tyre. (Tyre is in the country of Lebanon.) He was taken to the "Divine Abode" and given access to all wisdom and riches. However, he misused his wisdom and defiled the temples. It is believed that the "Divine Abode" was heaven. (*Ezekial* 28: 12-19)

Another ascension to the "Abode of the Gods" was made by a man named Gilgamesh, the ruler of Uruk, in Sumer. The story is told in a Sumerian tale called *The Epic of Gilgamesh*. King Gilgamesh's father was a human and his mother a goddess (an Elohim!). The description in the ancient text tells of what seems to be a space flight that he made:

> The heavens shrieked,
> The earth boomed,
> Lightning flashed,
> Daylight failed, darkness came.

That sounds like a rocket ship taking off and reaching the atmosphere, where everything is dark. Gilgamesh was traveling to the "Abode of the Gods," heaven.

There were other ascensions, but you probably don't want to read about them all. I think we can conclude that ancient peoples of the Middle East were familiar with ascension.

So, what did Jesus do?

Following His resurrection, He stayed here on earth for forty days, in a physical body. People touched Him, He talked with them, and He ate food (111). Then, He ascended into heaven in His physical body. It says this in the New Testament, in *Luke, Mark, Acts of the Apostles, Hebrews, Ephesians, Peter,* and other sources[112,113]. How did Jesus ascend?

In *Luke*, Jesus "parted from them and was carried up into heaven. And they…returned to Jerusalem in great joy." (*Luke* 24:51-52) "They" refers to the apostles.

The apostle Mark writes: "So then the Lord, after he had spoke to them, was taken up into heaven, and sits at the right hand of God." (*Mark* 16:19)

The *Acts of the Apostles* has a slightly longer accounting. "He was taken up before their very eyes, and a cloud hid Him from their sight. And while they were gazing up to heaven as he went, behold, two men stood by them in white garments and said to them, 'Men of Galilee, why do you stand looking up to heaven? This Jesus who has been taken up from you into heaven, shall come in the same way as you have seen him going to heaven.'" (*Acts* 1:9-11)

OK. In my church, the priest always said in his sermons that Jesus was taken up to heaven in a cloud. That's not exactly what the scriptures say. The scriptures say a cloud hid Jesus from the sight of the apostles. In my opinion, that sounds like the exhaust cloud produced by an aircraft taking off, or it could be that it flew into and above the clouds, where the apostles could no longer see Jesus.

Jesus, in a physical body, could not survive going much higher than the clouds, unless he was in an aircraft. Two angels, Elohim, told the apostles that Jesus will return in the same way.

In *Mark* and *Luke*, Jesus was "taken up" into heaven. Jesus didn't go on His own. Someone or something took Him up to heaven.

So to me, it makes sense that Jesus left in some type of vehicle that flies. I think He was going to heaven—Planet X. He will return one day in the same way, as the angels stated, in a vehicle that flies.

That makes more sense than Jesus being lifted up by a cloud and going out of sight, in a physical body. And all of the other ascensions in my research were journeys to Planet X, in some type of vehicle that flies.

One more important fact: Planet X was near the Earth during the life of Jesus. So it would have been accessible for space travel.

I tried to explain this to Lisa. She said I needed to find more proof to convince her. She believes Jesus went up to heaven in a cloud, not a flying vehicle. And she knows quantum physics too! I guess if you are a lifelong Christian like Lisa and me, this is a little too much for you.

More proof. OK: I found a Web site[115] which claims seventy verses in the Bible describe flying vehicles as clouds. Here are some of them:

1. *Exodus* 24:18: "Moses went into the midst of a cloud, and gat him up to the mount."
2. *Numbers* 9:17: "[A]nd in the place where the cloud abode, there the children of Israel pitched their tents."

3. *Exodus* 16:10: "[T]hey looked toward the wilderness, and behold, the glory of the Lord appeared in a cloud."

4. *Numbers* 9:21: "The cloud was taken up in the morning, then they journeyed."

5. *1 Kings* 18:44: "Behold, there ariseth a little cloud out of the sea."

6. *Deuteronomy* 1:33: "[W]ho went in the way before you…in fire by night…and in a cloud by day."

7. *Numbers* 10:11: "[A]nd the cloud rested in the wilderness of Paran."

In my opinion, the reason a cloud was mentioned in the Ascension of Jesus is because He was taken to heaven in a vehicle that flies, like all of the other ascensions.

Lisa still refused to accept it. To clarify, it's not that Lisa didn't believe, she wouldn't believe.

The Arraignment of Saddam Hussein

It was July 1, 2004. Saddam Hussein was brought before a tribunal to face charges against him. The arraignment was televised all over the Middle East. Saddam had grown a thick beard, and looked tired and nervous. An Iraqi judge read the charges against him:

1. Invading Kuwait
2. Gassing the Kurds in Halabja
3. Killing of religious figures
4. Killing of the Kurdish Barzani clan
5. Killing members of rival political parties
6. Brutal suppression and killing of Shiite Moslems
7. The Anfal campaign of displacing Kurds

Fatima said the spectacle of Saddam on trial was very surprising. Most Iraqis had come to fear the sight of Saddam Hussein, and here he was, nervous, with bags under his eyes, on trial.

Saddam said some bizarre things to the judge. He said he invaded Kuwait for the Iraqi people. The Kuwaitis are dogs. They caused the price of oil go down, making the Iraqis poor. He said the Kuwaitis were trying to turn Iraqi women into prostitutes.

Saddam claimed he did not know about the gassing of the Kurds until he saw it on television.

Nothing was mentioned about the fact that Saddam had taken billions of dollars from the Iraqi people. He constructed many palaces to glorify himself, while some of his people starved.

Saddam had acted like one of the gods of Sumer! He killed those who did not worship him. He led his people to slaughter in the Iran-Iraq War, the invasion of Kuwait, the Gulf War, and the campaigns against the Kurds and Shiites.

His trial was scheduled to begin in October, 2005. [123]

Prayer

Well, I guessed I was ready to talk to Old One for the last time. My departure was scheduled for July 4, Independence Day. Before I tell you about my last meeting with Old One, I want to share something with you.

After learning all of this, I began to wonder about praying to God. Jesus prayed, but to whom? Right before Jesus was arrested, He went to the Garden of Gesthemani and prayed. He knew what was going to happen to Him, asking that this "cup" be taken away. Who was Jesus praying to? Was it Yahweh, the Elohim?

Jesus taught the apostles a prayer, the "Our Father." Pay close attention to the words:

> Our Father, who art in Heaven,
> Hallowed be thy name.
> Thy kingdom come, Thy will be done.
> On earth as it is in Heaven. (*Matthew* 6:9-13)

The original version in Hebrew is translated as *may you continue establishing your kingdom,* instead of *Thy kingdom come.*

Does this mean the gods on Planet X will establish a kingdom on earth? It doesn't seem to be saying we will go to heaven, but rather that they will come here.

I began to worry that maybe we are praying to no one, or extraterrestrials, but I know praying really does work. I have had many prayers answered. Here are three prayer experiments I read about:

1. In 1995, at San Francisco General Hospital, cardiologist Randolf

Byrd studied thirty-nine coronary patients. Some were prayed for by home groups. Others were not. The prayed for patients were: significantly less likely to require antibodies (three versus sixteen), significantly less likely to develop edema (six versus eighteen), and significantly less likely to require a breathing tube (zero versus twelve).

2. In 1998, at the Pacific College of Medicine, psychiatrist Dr. Elizabeth Targ conducted a prayer test on critically ill AIDS patients. Twenty patients received about the same medical treatment. Half were prayed for by spiritual healers. Half were not. All ten of the prayed-for patients lived. Four who had not been prayed for died.

3. In 1999, at the Mid America Heart Institute, Drs. William Harris and James O'Keefe conducted prayer tests on 940 heart patients. The patients who were prayed for had eleven percent fewer heart attacks, strokes, and complications[125].

Someone is answering prayers. In my opinion, it is not Yahweh, the God of the Israelites. The results of the prayer experiments were reassuring for me.

The Truth I

It was July 3. I was ready to see Old One. For some reason, I was very nervous about this. Our last meeting. The last time I would talk to Old One. I walked into the museum for the last time. Old One was reading a manuscript he held in his hand. No lights were on in the museum. The only light was from the small windows, which did not have any blinds on them.

Every muscle in my body was tense. I stopped walking about three feet from Old One and began to speak.

"Hello Sir."

Old One looked at me.

"Um, I have completed the resurrection and ascension of Jesus and, you know, I'm leaving tomorrow." I paused. "So this is probably the last time that we will talk to each other." I paused again. Old One kept looking at me with no expression, like he usually does.

"Um, there were many resurrections before Jesus. The Elohim were able to resurrect people if they haven't been dead too long. They resurrected Jesus." I waited, hoping for a reaction from Old One to give me a clue about whether I was correct or not. Old One was perfectly still, like a statue in the museum.

"A dead person can't resurrect himself. Someone has to do it. Two angels in the tomb of Jesus did it, just like with Inanna, the goddess of Sumer."

Old One still did not say anything, looking down at the ground when I mentioned Inanna.

"Jesus was taken into heaven by a vehicle that flies, not by a cloud like

I was told. Yahweh flew around in a vehicle described as a cloud in the Bible. Others have been taken to heaven, such as Elijah taken by a whirlwind. That sounds like a helicopter-type vehicle. Jesus will return the same way He left." I looked at Old One for a minute. "Uh, that's it. Now I'm ready for the truth." Oops—maybe I shouldn't have said that. "Oh, and heaven is Planet X; at least it was in ancient times." That entered my brain really fast and just came right out of my mouth!

Old One took a deep breath, and began to speak. "I believe you are ready for the truth. I have written it for you." He held out something that looked like an old manuscript. "You may take this. But do not read this until you are at home."

I took the manuscript. "OK, I guess. Thank you, very much. Um, this has been very…enlightening. Things will never be the same for me."

Old One nodded his head and put his finger in the air, looking like he was posing for a sculpture. "No, they won't," he agreed. "The truth will set you free."

He put his hand back down by his side. We stood there without speaking for a minute. Then Old One said with a twinkle in his eye, "The Tower of Babel?"

"Yes, there was a Tower of Babel," I said.

"Go in peace, Joy DiNardo. Ayyamkum Saeeda. May your days be happy."

I detected a slight smile on his face. I put my hand out to shake Old One's hand. "I enjoyed working with you."

Old One did not shake my hand. I looked up at his eyes. He towered over me by at least two feet. Old One bowed towards me. So I did the same thing. Then I turned and walked away, stopping at the door and looking at him one more time. He had sat down and was looking out of a window. I felt sad. Turning again, I walked out of the museum.

I enjoyed working with you? Why do I always say such goofy things? I whispered "goodbye" again.

Goodbye

I won't bore you with the long good-byes to everyone. I spent the evening of July 3 feeling sad, sometimes letting a tear come out. I will never see Fatima again. I will miss Lisa and Ricky very much, although I hope to see them again someday.

Strangely enough, I will miss Babylon, Iraq. It was unbearably hot today, 112 degrees. I was sick of sand and bugs. But there was something about Babylon, something almost spiritual. I can't quite put my finger on it. It's like my soul connects with this place: Babylon, the Euphrates River. Something deep inside of me feels comfortable here.

The Truth II

It was a long trip home. I was flown to the U.S. Air Force base in Frankfort, Germany. The temperature at Frankfort was sixty-eight degrees when we landed. That used to be a pleasant temperature. Now it seemed cold.

I had about three hours to wait before my flight to New York. I also had the manuscript from Old One in my carry-on bag. Old One said not to read it until I was at home. Should I or shouldn't I?

Well, I did it. I opened the manuscript. The pages were almost a brown color, like some type of parchment paper. They were rough to touch, sturdier than regular paper. Old One had written in English, thank the gods, all of them. He wrote in an exaggerated type of penmanship, like some of the signatures on the Declaration of Independence. Each page was filled from top to bottom with writing in black ink. He only wrote on one side of each page, and there were about one hundred pages. Hmm…one hundred pages to tell the truth.

The pages were bound by a leather string, like some ancient manuscript to be read and revered for many generations to come. I opened the first page and noticed a little folder on the inside cover. I hadn't noticed before the folded piece of paper sticking out. It was a map of the stars, superimposed over a map of the earth. The names of some of the star patterns were written on it, along with the names of some countries. The Pleadies star group was written in big bold letters.

The star map—this was amazing to me. *The Urantia Book* had said we have made contact with beings from the Pleiades. The Pleiades are mentioned three times in the Bible. In *Amos* 5:8 it says "The Creator is the Master of the Pleiades."

On the map, the North Star was placed at the North Pole, and this happened to the star patterns:

1. The Pleiades fell over Egypt. The Pleiades used to be known as Khema. Egypt used to be known as the land of Khem.
2. The center of the star map was at the Great Pyramid at Giza, Egypt.
3. The stars that form Taurus the Bull fell over the Taurus Mountains in Turkey.
4. Ursa Major, the Great Bear Star, fell over Russia.
5. Aries the Ram fell over Rome.
6. Aquila the Eagle fell over the United States.
7. Draco the Dragon fell over China.
8. Orion the Warrior fell over Iraq.

These star patterns are all the symbols of those countries today. The American Eagle, the Russian Bear, the Chinese Dragon...They were determined thousands of years ago by ancient astronomers—the Elohim[126]? I think that's what Old One was trying to tell me.

I tucked the map away and looked at the first page. It began:
Joy DiNardo, you have come to me seeking the Truth.
What? I hadn't gone to him! That upset me. He had a lot of nerve writing that. He's the one who started the whole thing. I was just minding my business, touring the ruins of Babylon, and he jumped into my conversation about the Tower of Babel. Great. Now I couldn't show this to anyone. It sounded like I was stumbling around Iraq searching for the Truth. Everyone at home already thought something was wrong with me.

They didn't understand why I wasn't interested in getting married. Also, doing Yoga and meditating all the time didn't help, along with the candles and aromatherapy dispensers in my townhouse. My sisters say I am like a sorcerer or something. I grew herbs too. One time I went to a hypnotist to find out if I had a past life but I couldn't relax enough to be hypnotized. Now I was in Iraq meeting with a mysterious "Old One" who dressed in a tunic, trying to find the truth. This will make it worse—Joy the weird sister.

I looked out the window at the airport. That's just great. After I calmed down, I continued reading.
It is curious that in your search for the Truth, you did not ask my name.

168

I was *not* searching for the Truth. Old One started the whole thing. I was perfectly happy before I met Old One. And, I was always afraid to ask his name. Old One was at least seven feet tall and made me feel like an idiot when I talked to him.

I had to quit arguing with each sentence. I continued reading.

I have signed my name at the end.

That was just great! Well, should I go to the last page or not? I sat there for about ten minutes, arguing with myself. Did Old One want me to go to the last page? He must, since he wrote this now. Then again, maybe he didn't, and that's why he wrote this now. Nothing is simple, not even the Truth.

I decided to put the manuscript away. Old One told me not to read it until I was at home. That's why this wasn't going too well. I shoved the papers back into my carry-on bag.

I was hungry! I began wandering around. A cantina nearby had Starbucks coffee. I couldn't believe it. Starbucks! I ordered a large coffee with a shot of espresso. It had been so long. I sat down to enjoy my Starbucks coffee. It tasted so good. Even though it was hot, I gulped it down in a few minutes. I had to order another one, this time with a double shot of espresso. I actually said "make it a double." I drank this one a little slower.

Now I had to go to the bathroom. Why did I do this? I was going to be in the bathroom on the airplane all the way to the States.

I ate dinner and developed a stomachache. Walking around, I found the bathroom. Finally, it was time to board the airplane. I'm slightly claustrophobic, on top of everything else. Spending hours on an airplane was difficult for me.

My seat was next to the window. I tried to talk to the elderly woman sitting next to me, discovering she worked for a magazine. When I mentioned that I had been in Iraq, she made a face and then didn't talk too much, drifting off to sleep before the plane left the runway.

So now I was sitting on this airplane. It was dark outside so I couldn't see anything out of the window, and the magazine lady next to me was snoring. I was wide-awake from the espresso. There was only one thing to do—read the manuscript. I pulled it back out of my carry-on bag, deciding not to look at the last page to see Old One's name. My mind concluded he mentioned it on the first page so I would avoid looking at the last page. My mind decided without me, while I was running around the airport drinking espresso and going to the bathroom.

OK, I started again.

Joy DiNardo, you have come to me seeking the Truth. It is curious that in your search for the Truth, you did not ask my name. I have signed my name at the end.

I will tell you now what is already known. It was written thousands of years ago.

In the beginning, the Creator thought of all things. There is a Creator of all. The Creator gave birth to many suns. Without the sun, nothing can exist. There can be no life, not even matter. And there was water. Without water, we cannot have the life of the sun.

The Solar System

Old One continued by explaining the formation of the solar system. The sun was formed first, and then the planets. But he wasn't talking about our solar system. He was talking about Planet X's solar system. According to Old One, Planet X is actually what we call a brown dwarf star. It is not very bright compared to our sun. The brown dwarf star has its own planets and orbits our sun.

So Planet X is really a star. Planet X has planets that revolve around it, as it revolves around the sun. We are actually part of a binary star system. "Binary" refers to the existence of two stars that revolve around each other: the sun and Planet X, which is a brown dwarf star[127,128].

Most stars are binary. I know this is true from astronomy class at Penn State. The frequent occurrence of binary stars was determined by the famous French astronomer Charles Messier.

We don't know our sun is part of a binary star system because most of the time Planet X is billions of miles away. Remember from *Genesis Revisited*, by Zecharia Sitchin, that in 1983, NASA detected heat from a heavenly body about fifty billion miles away. That was Planet X, the brown dwarf star!

Next, Old One talked about our solar system. According to Old One, all of the planets in our solar system had water on them when they formed. A planet between Mars and Jupiter was completely covered with water, but that planet is no longer there. Here is the reason: Planet X!

Billions of years ago, as Planet X came near our solar system, one of its planets collided with the planet between Mars and Jupiter. Half of the planet between Mars and Jupiter shattered and formed an asteroid belt. The asteroid belt still exists between Mars and Jupiter. The other half was pushed into a new orbit between Venus and Mars. This other half became Earth[129]!

That was a surprise to me. I didn't know whether to believe this or not. Then Old One wrote that there is something in the book of *Genesis* about the asteroid belt. The asteroid belt is mentioned in *Genesis* 1:6-7 [132] as "the firmament." "And God said: Let there be a firmament made amidst the waters: and let it divide the waters from the waters. And God made a firmament, and divided the waters that were under the firmament from those that were above the firmament, and it was so." (*Genesis* 1:6-7)

The firmament is the asteroid belt. The waters below the firmament/asteroid belt are on Venus, Earth, and Mars. The waters above the firmament/asteroid belt are on Jupiter, Saturn, Uranus, Neptune, and Pluto. Now, *Genesis*, Chapter 1, finally makes sense to me.

Zecharia Sitchin did a lot of research on this in his book, *Genesis Revisited*[133]. According to Mr. Sitchin:

1. Venus was observed by the Mariner 10 spacecraft and the Pioneer Venus I spacecraft. Scientists have concluded that Venus may at one time have been covered by water at an average depth of thirty feet. Venus has a thick atmosphere. It is mostly carbon dioxide, but it does contain water vapor.

2. Earth has water. About seventy percent of its surface is water.

3. Mars was observed by the Mariner 9 spacecraft and the Viking I and Viking II missions. The southern pole region of Mars consists of ice, and dried up riverbeds are all over the planet's surface.

4. Mercury was determined not to contain water by the Mariner 10 spacecraft. It is too close to the sun.

So, Venus, Earth, and Mars are the waters below the firmament/asteroid belt.

5. Jupiter was observed by the Pioneer 10 spacecraft. It was found to be surrounded by gases and droplets of water. There is ice on two of Jupiter's moons, Io and Gannymede.

6. Saturn was investigated by the Pioneer 11 spacecraft. Its ringlets consist of chunks of ice. Saturn's inner moons named Rhea, Janus, Mimas, Enceladus, and Dione have ice.

7. The Voyager II spacecraft concluded that Uranus had a gaseous atmosphere and is covered by icy water.

8. Neptune was also visited by Voyager II. It is believed to have a rocky core and is covered in ice.

9. Astronomers are not sure about Pluto yet. Some believe it is covered with ice.

So, Jupiter, Saturn, Uranus, Neptune, and maybe Pluto are the waters above the firmament/asteroid belt.

Remember, the asteroid belt is between Mars and Jupiter. It is the shattered remnants of half of a planet that used to exist between Mars and Jupiter. *Genesis* 1:6-7 called it "the firmament."

I believe Old One was correct about the asteroid belt.

Here's the shocking part. *Genesis* 1:8. "And God called the firmament, Heaven..."

So, Ricky was right. I was right. Old One was right. When the ancient peoples referred to the heavens, they meant up there, the asteroid belt, the planets.

Now, what about the Earth being the other half of the shattered planet between Mars and Jupiter? "God also said: Let the waters that are under the heaven, be gathered together into one place; and let the dry land appear. And it was so done." (*Genesis* 1:9)

The shattered planet was under the heaven, under the asteroid belt. It was originally completely covered with water. When it collided with one of the brown star's planets, it was split and part of the planet became land. The planet became the Earth[131,133,135].

Old One's story about the solar system appears to agree with the Bible—*Genesis* 1:6-9.

Old One continued to explain our binary star system. The brown dwarf star's orbit around the sun never comes closer than beyond Pluto. However, the planets and comets orbiting the brown dwarf star may cross into the paths of the sun's planets. This does not happen with each orbit. It depends on which side of the sun, and the brown dwarf star, that the planets and comets are on as they pass[135].

Old One wrote that the brown dwarf star has its own planets. Everything in the star system revolves in a clockwise motion. The brown dwarf star revolves around the sun clockwise, the sun's planets revolve around the sun clockwise, and the brown dwarf star's planets revolve around it clockwise. However, the clockwise motions of the planets around the brown dwarf star appear to be moving counter-clockwise when they are passing through the sun's system[134].

That was hard to follow, but it agrees with ancient Sumerian texts. According to Zecharia Sitchin, the texts say Planet X, which they called Nibiru, enters our solar system from the south, in a retrograde orbit. By retrograde, they probably mean counter-clockwise.

Other proof of this is the orbital perturbations of the sun's outer planets. Scientists have concluded that something is affecting their orbits. Our binary star system is affecting their orbits[130]!

Life and Evolution

Old One's writings did not have any breaks in them. There were no chapters, no headings, not even any paragraphs. It was just word after word, for one hundred pages.

Next, Old One talked about the beginning of life. Here is some of what Old One wrote about the origin of life:

Life cannot just begin. Some believe that they can create life. I assure you from a million years of knowledge, it is not possible. On Earth as it was in heaven, life was planted.

I wondered what he meant by a million years of knowledge. Old One went on to write that one-celled organisms existing on comets following the brown dwarf star were transferred to Earth during collisions with Earth, bringing life. The same thing happened to a planet orbiting the brown dwarf star. "On Earth as it was in Heaven[136]!"

This is contrary to some evolutionists who believe life on Earth started on its own. I did some research on this at home, reading about Charles Darwin's theories of evolution. He could not determine how life began, but speculated that nonliving chemicals, given the right amount of time and the right environment, could develop by themselves into living matter[137].

Another scientist, Walter Bradley, calculated the odds of that happening, saying, "If you took all of the carbon in the universe (we are made of carbon) and put it on the face of the Earth, and allowed it to chemically react at the most rapid rate possible for a billion years, the odds of creating one protein molecule (cells are made of protein molecules) would be one chance in ten with sixty zeros after it. And then, twenty protein molecules would have to assemble by themselves in the correct way to form one living cell."

Bradley said it is difficult to believe a living cell is the random product of unguided nature. It is more logical to conclude this is the work of an Intelligent Designer[138]. Old One called the Intelligent Designer the Creator of All Things.

Old One also said there is life on many other planets. In my opinion, it is impossible for life to be created randomly from nonliving chemicals in many places, given the odds against it happening just one time.

I found many writings and opinions that agree with Old One's statements. The Greek philosopher, Anaxagoras, around 500 BC, stated that "the seeds of life swarm through the universe, ready to sprout and create life wherever a proper environment is found." I think he meant life existed on comets, just as Old One had written. Sir Frederick Hoyle, a famous British astronomer, said life on Earth arrived on a comet about four billion years ago. Nobel Prize winner Manfred Eigen stated that a primordial gene appeared 3.89 billion years ago, and this would be possible "only in the case of an extraterrestrial origin[139]."

These scientists and philosophers agree with Old One. Life on Earth, and in the heavens, came from comets as one-celled organisms[140].

Old One continued the story. He said the one-celled organisms, or seeds from space, eventually evolved into algae. The algae populated the seas and the land on Earth, changing the atmosphere by using up carbon dioxide gases and creating oxygen, which paved the way for animals to develop[141,142].

Old One gave the order of evolution: plants, sea creatures, creatures that crawl and birds, and land animals.

Old One said birds evolved directly from sea creatures, not land animals. From what I've read, most evolutionists say the opposite. I believe Old One because my Bible says the same thing in *Genesis* 1:20: "God also said: Let the waters bring forth the creeping creatures having life, and the fowl that may fly over the Earth."

The waters brought forth the fowl that may fly over the Earth. Birds evolved from sea creatures.

The Elohim

Old One did not continue the story of evolution all the way to the creation of man. Instead, he began telling a very strange story.

There is a life-giving planet that orbits the brown dwarf star.

He called the planet heaven.

It is the home of the gods. On heaven are magnificent temples, and feasts of plenty.

Old One went on and on elaborating about how wonderful the planet "heaven" is. It was what we would imagine heaven to be. Then he said that gods lived on heaven and he began to describe them. At this point, I put the manuscript down. I started to think; these were not really gods, they were flesh and blood beings. Old One was describing a civilization that existed on a planet that orbited the brown dwarf star; the star that orbits the sun. Old One said this is the truth. It is so incredible, I don't know whether I can believe this. Why doesn't everyone know about this if it is true? I picked the manuscript back up.

Old One said the "Father" in heaven was named Anu. This Anu was the king in heaven, "seated on the throne[143]."

Then Old One deviated a little bit and described the appearance of the gods. Their skin and hair was light, their eyes gray or blue, and they were tall—ten, eleven, twelve, even fifteen feet tall[144]. These towering gods could live for thousands of years and had an advanced civilization with amazing capabilities, such as growing massive quantities of food in small areas and moving large objects by negating the force of gravity. They could travel in space, and communicated sometimes without speaking over great distances. So compared to us, they were gods!

Old One's story became even stranger. The gods journeyed to Earth during one of their planet's close orbits to find gold[145].

So that is why gold was important! That was the first thing Old One had asked me about.

Old One described the gods' journeys to Earth. They came in groups of fifty. Their names were Enki, Marduk, Ninhursag, Enlil, Alalu, Inanna, and many others. The gods of Sumer[147]!

One of the groups crashed. Fifty gods flew too close to Jupiter, destroying their spacecraft and killing everyone aboard. Evidently, the gods were not indestructible[148].

The gods established a settlement on Earth and called it Eridu. The settlement was in Iraq, between the Tigris and Euphrates Rivers. Eridu meant "home in the faraway." Eridu is the name from which the word *earth* is derived. It is *Erde* in German, *Erthe* in Middle English, *Erd* in Kurdish, *Ereds* in Aramaic, and *Eretz* in Hebrew. These names all derived from Eridu. So our Earth is the "home in the faraway[146]."

The god Marduk established a way station on Mars. It was a staging area to transport gold from Earth to heaven[149].

The gods came to be called Anunnaki, a Sumerian word meaning "those who from heaven came down to Earth." Old One wrote this:

The day that the gods landed was a day of destiny for the Earth. From then it was on Earth as it was in heaven.

Old One wrote like the writers of the Bible, or like Jesus spoke. That was very curious.

Old One's story continued. The gods measured time by the revolutions of the brown dwarf star around the sun. According to Zecharia Sitchin, it took about 3,600 years for Nibiru (the brown dwarf star) to revolve around the sun one time. So one year for the gods would be 3,600 Earth years. Old One wrote that the gods came here 120 years before the great flood (Noah's Flood). He meant 120 god years, which is 432,000 Earth years. So, they came here 432,000 years before Noah's Flood!

Here's something amazing I found out later at home. The Hindus have a divine period of time called a "Yuga." One "Yuga" is 432,000 years! There is only one place they could have gotten this from: the time period from the landing of the gods to Noah's Flood. That's where the Hindus came up with the "Yuga." (151)

Also, in *Genesis* 6:3 of the Bible, it quotes God, or the Elohim, as saying: "My spirit shall not dwell with humanity forever…their days shall be 120 years."

Those were god years. That's how long the gods were here between the first landing and Noah's Flood—120 god years, or 432,000 Earth years. That's how long they dwelt on Earth. It appears Old One's dating was correct.

Next, Old One told the story of a battle between two leaders of the gods. The loser was banished to the way station on Mars, where he died. In honor of this god, his face was carved into a mountain on Mars[150].

Something about that story was familiar. I think I remember something about the "face on Mars." Or am I thinking of the "man in the moon?" No, I think NASA had taken pictures of a rock formation that looked like a face on the surface of Mars! When I arrived home and settled in, one of the first things I did was to send an e-mail to Becky at the Space Center asking her about the "face on Mars." I hoped it wasn't going to be classified information again. Here is Becky's e-mail back to me:

Joy, it's a coincidence that I was just watching a video of a speech George Bush, Sr. had made in 1989. We have the video here at the Space Center. He was talking about making plans for a mission to Mars with a manned spacecraft. George Bush, Sr. said we will be going 'back to the future.' Maybe he was referring to the movie Back to the Future. *But maybe he meant something else, like going to the future involves something from the past[152].*

Here's what I know. The Mariner 9 and the Voyager 1 and Voyager 2 spacecrafts scanned almost the entire surface of Mars in the 1970s and sent back pictures. There is an area on Mars we have named Cydonia. The pictures in that area showed structures that do not appear to be natural.

Near the structures is a rock formation two miles long and about a half mile high. The picture appears to show that it has the features of a face, a human looking face, a man's face. The man appears to be wearing a helmet, his mouth is slightly open, and his eyes are looking straight out into space. The pictures caused quite a controversy. Some scientists and astronomers were calling for future missions to the 'face on Mars.' NASA took the position that it was just a rock and its resemblance to a face was a coincidence."

NASA scientists and astronomers have issued a series of pronouncements stating it is a mountain, not a face. No further missions to the area of the 'face' were scheduled. However, in 2001, the Mars Orbital Camera took new pictures. In 2002, the Mars Odyssey took more pictures. They show a two-mile raised area. These pictures are more defined, more 'up close' than the originals from the 1970s. The new pictures do not show features of a face. They show a weathered, rocky, raised structure. It still does not look natural to me. It is a raised structure on a flat plain. NASA took the position that the new pictures confirmed it was not a face and won't say any more[153].

The whole thing was very suspicious. It's like the 'face on Mars' and the structures are classified information. They're not, officially. But in practice, they are. No one here will say too much about them. In my opinion, George Bush, Sr. knows there is a face, or at least unnatural structures. That's why he wanted to go to Mars. George Bush, Jr. has been talking about a mission to Mars too.

Well, I think that gives some credibility to Old One's story again. The "face on Mars" may belong to one of the gods, an Anunnaki. The structures on Mars may be the remnants of the way station the gods built to transport gold many thousands of years ago.

Old One continued his story about the gods.

The Gods created magnificent cities on Earth. One place was called Nippur. It was a mission control center located in the Sinai Desert. Other places included: Larak, a beacon city to guide landing spacecraft; Shuruppak, a medical center; and a botanical garden called Eden. The gods, the Anunnaki, created the Garden of Eden[153].

The Anunnaki were the Elohim of the Bible! I put the manuscript down. I had to take a break because I felt a little shaken. I had suspected this before, but it hit me now like a brick. Everything I had been taught before was not true, or maybe better words would be distorted, misinterpreted. If I am to believe what Old One has written, it would mean billions of people believe misinterpretations of the Bible and other ancient writings.

According to Old One, there is a Creator, but this Creator is not the God of the Bible who created the Garden of Eden. The Anunnaki did it. The gods of Sumer.

I know what is coming. The gods of Sumer, the Anunnaki, probably did everything in the Bible. Yahweh, the God of the Old Testament was one of them. The angel Gabriel who dictated the Quran to Mohammed and announced the birth of Jesus to Mary was one of them. An Anunnaki. One who from heaven came down to Earth—in a spacecraft.

It's hard to believe that billions of people, including me, have been misled. I was tired. I closed my eyes and fell into a dark sleep. I don't remember dreaming. It was one of those deep sleeps where all you remember is darkness, like you've fallen into a hole and can't get out.

Coffee

I slept deeply for the next few hours. Gradually, the smell of coffee penetrated my dormant brain. It tingled my frontal lobe, bringing me to consciousness again. I opened my eyes; everything was fuzzy. Then Magazine Lady came into focus. She was drinking coffee. My brain woke up.

"Where are we?" I blurted out. Then I noticed I was drooling. How embarrassing!

Magazine Lady said we were about three hours from New York. I had been asleep for a long time.

Bathroom feelings suddenly took over my body. I had to go to the bathroom, but I was afraid to ask Magazine Lady to get up to let me out. She had her coffee and some magazines arranged across the tray over her lap so I decided to hold it.

I started thinking about all the information I had just read. Who could I tell about the gods from Planet X, the Anunnaki? No one will believe me. Yeah, right, Joy. The God of the Bible was from another planet. I can just hear them now. "Joy, you're nuts. What happened to you in Iraq?"

Suddenly, I couldn't hold it anymore. I had to ask Magazine Lady to let me out to go to the bathroom. She sighed, picked up her coffee, and acted like she was doing a great service to humanity by getting up. As I passed her, I bumped her arm and some of the coffee spilled on her pants. Great!

I blurted out "Oops, sorry, I'm sorry."

"Jesus Christ. It got on my pants," she exclaimed at the same time.

I said I was sorry again and asked if she wanted to go to the bathroom ahead of me to wipe it off.

"Forget it. I'll just smell like coffee and have stained pants." She plopped back down in her seat. I wanted to tell her that she smelled like coffee before it spilled on her pants.

Coming back from the bathroom, I began to worry. I was going to have to ask Magazine Lady to move again. My forehead and nose wrinkled as I prepared for another confrontation. Then I noticed Magazine Lady had moved. Her seat was vacant. I looked around and saw her three seats back. Now I was glad I had drooled. I should have drooled on her. But my Christian up-bringing kicked in like it always does and I feel guilty when my brain has those kinds of thoughts. But remember Karma. She will have to pay for being so rude.

I sat down. Another two hours until landing. Home! I thought about home—my townhouse, my car, my coffeemaker. I could go for some coffee. I asked the stewardess to bring some. Then the manuscript sticking out of my carry-on caught my eye.

The Creation of Man

Old One's story continued.

The Anunnaki tried to extract gold from the waters of the Tigris and Euphrates Rivers, and from the Persian Gulf. The process did not produce sufficient quantities of gold. They decided to mine the gold from the ground in South Africa.

My mind made the connection. When the South Africans wanted to find gold, they looked for abandoned mines. Whenever they dug near an abandoned mine, they would find gold. Items in the abandoned mines were carbon dated to be tens of thousands of years old. I remembered this from *Genesis Revisited*, by Zecharia Sitchin. The abandoned mines had been dug by the Anunnaki! The book I had laughed at was correct. Old One said the Anunnaki carried out the backbreaking work for many thousands of years in the mines until their discontent grew so great that the Anunnaki gold miners refused to work. So a meeting was called of the Anunnaki leaders. Enki (remember him? the medicine man) and Ninhursag (the nurse) had a solution. They noted that hominids roamed the areas around the mines in South Africa. They could genetically alter the hominids to be more like the Anunnaki, more like the gods. Then the hominids could take over the work in the mines[154].

Enki and Ninhursag would recreate the hominids in their image and their likeness, the image and likeness of the Anunnaki! That would mean increasing their intelligence by increasing their brain size, giving them the ability to speak, and making them able to walk more upright. They would accomplish this by mixing hominid genes with Anunnaki genes[156].

Another Anunnaki leader, Enlil, was against this. He said only the Creator of All Things should bring forth new species, in the natural way.

Enlil finally agreed, on two conditions. The first was that Enki would not give the new creatures the ability to reproduce. The second was that its life span would be much shorter than the Anunnaki's. These two conditions became the Tree of Knowledge and the Tree of Life in the Bible. The new hybrid creature would not have the knowledge of sex and reproduction, nor everlasting life, like the gods, the Annunaki[157].

Enki agreed to Enlil's terms. He created man and woman in South Africa by mixing the genes of a female hominid with the genes of a male Anunnaki. That is why there is no missing link. Hominids did not evolve into us. We were created by Enki, the doctor. We were created by the gods of Planet X, the gods of Sumer!

The new creatures were called *adamus*, which is a Sumerian word meaning "workers." That is where the name Adam came from! It says in *Genesis* 5:2: "He created them male and female; and blessed them: and called their name Adam, in the day they were created."

Old One wrote that *adamus* were also called *lulus*, which meant "mixed ones." The *lulus* were often treated badly by their Anunnaki creators[160].

At home, I found out a South African Zulu medicine man, Credo Mutwa, has preserved an ancient Zulu story. The story says artificially created slaves, made by aliens, worked the gold mines[161]!

So there we have it. We were created by Enki and Ninhursag, Anunnakis, to be their worker-slaves! It made me feel angry to think we were designed to be a race of slaves.

At home, I discovered this whole story could be found in a Sumerian writing called the *"Atra Hasis Epic,"* and also in the Bible: "And God said, 'Let us make man in our image, after our likeness…' So God created man in His image, in the image of God created He him; male and female He created them." (*Genesis* 1:26-27)

"Us" and "our" refer to the Anunnaki, the Elohim, the gods of Sumer and Planet X. "God" refers to Enki.

To create adamus was a difficult process. A hominid embryo had to be obtained, fertilized by a male Anunnaki, and placed in the womb of a female Anunnaki, who carried the embryo to birth. That was a time-consuming process. Therefore, in the botanical garden called Eden, Enki decided to give the adamu the ability to reproduce. This is the story you know as the Tree of Knowledge, and Adam's rib. A male adamu was brought to the Garden of Eden to work. Then a female adamu was brought to Eden and genetically altered to be able to reproduce[155].

Old One wrote Enlil was very upset when he discovered this. Enlil was the god in the Garden of Eden who talked to Adam and Eve, and asked why they were wearing clothes. (*Genesis* 3:9-12)

Enlil banished the male *adamu* and the female *adamu*, who could now reproduce, from the Garden of Eden. Enlil had to do this before they could eat from the Tree of Life, which was the ability to live thousands of years, like the Anunnaki—everlasting life[158].

Enlil told the *adamus* that the land outside of the Garden of Eden would be difficult to cultivate: "In sorrow thou shalt bring forth children … cursed in the earth in thy work; thorns and thistles shall it bring forth to thee … In the sweat of thy face shalt thou eat bread." (*Genesis* 3:16-19)

It would not be a paradise as it was in the Garden of Eden. Their life would be harsh—backbreaking work to survive, and great pain in child-bearing[159].

This happened two hundred thousand years ago. Fossil records and Mitochondrial DNA evidence support this. The Bible tells the same story as Old One.

Old One wrote that Enki made a lot of mistakes in the creation of humans. We seem to have many more genetic disorders than animals have, more than fossil evidence suggests that hominids had, and more than the Anunnaki suffered from. Humans have over fifteen thousand genetic disorders.

When I had a chance at home, I looked up genetic disorders on the Internet and discovered thousands of them. Three to five percent of all births have genetic malformations. Some DNA researchers believe all non-infectious diseases are genetic disorders. I have some examples:

1. Sickle Cell Anemia: a genetic mutation in blood protein that affects organs and causes great pain, and can cause strokes. It affects 1 in every 375 people of African descent.

2. Gaucher Disease: a defective genetic blueprint for an enzyme that causes a breakdown in liver and spleen. It affects 1 in 10 Ashkenazi Jews. These are Jewish peoples whose ancestors were from Northern Europe.

3. Cystic Fibrosis: a specific gene inherited and causing coughing, wheezing, and abdominal pains. It affects 1 in every 3,300 whites, 1 in every 8,000 blacks, and 1 in 10,000 Native Americans.

4. Huntington Disease: a larger than normal Huntington gene, mapped to chromosome number four, which kills brain cells in middle age. It affects 1 in 20,000 people.

5. Fragile X Syndrome: a mutation of a gene on the X chromosome, causing impaired learning, short attention spans, long, narrow faces, and prominent ears and forehead. It affects 1 in every 2,000 males.

6. Tay Sachs: a mutation on the Hex A-gene, it causes muscle weakness, slurred speech, and even death. It affects 1 in 27 people of Jewish descent.

It is believed at least fifteen percent of all cancers and ten percent of all acute chronic diseases have a genetic component. There are thousands of these defects. Old One wrote that they were the results of mistakes and unexpected occurrences during the combining of Anunnaki DNA and hominid DNA[162].

Not only are we a slave race, we have many genetic defects.

Enki continued to experiment with humans, creating Neanderthals. The experiments continued even after the Great Flood. If you have ever wondered how the four-foot pygmies could develop nearby the Masai Tribe, whose average height is six-foot-two, according to Old One the answer is Enki and his experiments. A Mayan holy book, the *Popol Vuh*, states that "various forms of life are from unsuccessful attempts by gods to make people[163]."

The Tree of Life

We have another genetic limitation deliberately inserted into our DNA makeup. Healthy body cells are programmed to divide many times during a lifetime. Dividing is what produces new healthy cells for our body. But this process of division and replication is finite, so a non-dividing state is ultimately reached. Then the cells become damaged, and that is the process of aging.

The division of cells is controlled by caps at the end of DNA strands. These caps are called the telomeres. As each cell divides, a piece of telomere is lost. The dividing process ceases when the telomeres become too short. Then there is no new cell division and replication, and all that follows is deterioration, which is old age.

Laboratory experiments with tissue samples have shown the application of the genetic enzyme telomerase can prevent telomere shortening upon cell division and replication. So, theoretically, if we prevent telomere shortening, body cells could continue to divide indefinitely[164].

Old One wrote:

If we did not have this defect of shortening telomeres, we would have "everlasting life," like the Annunaki. This was the Tree of Life Enlil did not want Adam and Eve to eat the fruit of. The Annunaki knew how to reverse this defect, but Enlil did not permit it. He banished Adam and Eve from the Garden of Eden before Enki could give us "everlasting life."

Cain and Abel

Next, Old One wrote about Cain and Abel, the sons of Adam and Eve in the Bible. But his story was quite different from the Bible version.

The humans continued to reproduce and increase their numbers. After a period of time, Enki impregnated two human females. This was both lust on the part of Enki and an experiment. Enki wanted to use his genes to perfect humans! Enki discovered humans were compatible with the gods and could produce offspring together.

The human females had a son and a daughter—Enki's children. He called the boy Adapa, and the girl Titi, bringing them to Eridu, the settlement in Iraq.

According to Old One, Adapa and Titi were the Biblical Adam and Eve. They were a new, improved race of humans—Enki's offspring. They were the first Homo sapien sapiens, from whom we descended[165].

Adapa was the first person on the *Sumerian King's List* and the first human to ascend to heaven. He was sent to the planet that orbits the brown dwarf star to acquire knowledge about heaven and earth.

The Anunnaki have no taboos against conception between brothers and sisters, fathers and daughters, and other relatives. So, when Titi came of age, she had a son—by Enki. This son was named Cain. She had a second son who was conceived by Adapa, and he was named Abel! Therefore, Cain had an Anunnaki father, a god—Enki. Abel's father was part human—Adapa[166]. That was the source of their rivalry, the story of Cain and Abel.

I didn't know whether to believe this version of the story of Cain and Abel. *Genesis* 4:1-2 gives us clues that agree Enki was Cain's father: "And Adam knew Eve his wife: who conceived and brought forth Cain, saying: I have gotten a man through God. And again she brought forth his brother Abel."

If you read carefully, it is saying Adam knew Eve after she had conceived and brought forth Cain. She brought forth Cain through God—Enki. Enki, the god who gave humans the ability to reproduce. Enki was the father of Eve's child, Cain. Eve, according to Old One, was Titi.

In the New Testament, in *I John* 3:12, it says: "Cain was born of the wicked one, and slew his brother." The wicked one is the Serpent in the Garden of Eden who gave Eve the fruit of the Tree of Knowledge. That was Enki[167]!

Cain felt he should be favored because he was more Anunnaki than Abel. But Enki seemed to favor Abel. Cain could not accept this. He killed Abel in a fit of jealousy. Cain had to be punished by the Anunnaki so *Genesis* 4:16 tells of how he was banished from Eridu. "Cain went out from the presence of the Lord, and dwelt in the land of Nod, east of Eden."

Old One said Cain was banished to a wilderness area to the east, around what is now the country of Yemen.

I was curious about what the Bible called the land of Nod. When I was at home, I tried to find information on the land of Nod. It sounds like a magical, mysterious place. The land of Nod.

I found out Biblical scholars are in complete disagreement about where the land of Nod is located. The Bible only says it is to the east of Eden. To me, that sounds like it was nearby, to the east. It could be in the country of Yemen, as Old One wrote. Yemen is east of Iraq, where both Eridu and Eden were located. Some scholars placed Nod as far east as the Americas. Others say it was not an actual place. The word Nod came from the Hebrew word "nwd," which means to wander, so it simply meant Cain became a wanderer[168].

The Bible, in *Genesis* 4:17-24, goes on to say Cain married and had a son named Enoch. Cain built a city and named it after his son. Then it lists the next seven descendants of Cain. So, Cain could not have become a wanderer, since he built a city and the writers of the Bible were able to keep track of his descendants.

The only explanation I found that made sense was from Samaritan writings. The Samaritans were a tribe that lived near the Israelites in the time of Jesus. The Samaritans have their own version of the first five books of the Bible. The Samaritan texts say Cain was banished to the "Land of Keli." There is a great sand-swept wilderness in northeastern Yemen called the Ar Rub Al Khali. That means the "Empty Quarter." Some scholars believe the Land of Keli is Khali[169,170].

Old One wrote that the story of Cain and Abel explains a lot about us, human beings. The degree of Annunaki ancestry has been the most divisive issue among humans. More Anunnaki ancestry is desirable. Keep in mind, the Anunnaki were light skinned, had brown or light-colored hair, gray or bluish eyes that were large and round, and were tall[171].

This is the source of prejudice against darker skin colors. It goes all the way back to the Anunnaki. When the Nazis claimed that tall Germans with blond hair, blue eyes, and fair skin were superior to all other races, it is because of the Anunnaki. The more one looks like an Anunnaki, the more superior they are. The Hindu caste system makes lighter skinned people a higher caste. The white Brahman priests, the lightest skinned peoples in southern Asia, were the highest caste. They resembled the Anunnaki more than any other peoples in southern Asia[172].

This all began with the rivalry between Cain and Abel. Cain thought he was superior because he had more Anunnaki ancestry!

The Great Flood

The leader of the Anunnaki, Enlil, was very angry about the prolifera-tion of humans, complaining they were everywhere. The sounds of their mating kept him awake at night. Enlil tried to control the human popula-tion by introducing diseases and plagues. Also, there were times of drought, floods, and earthquakes coinciding with the passings of the brown dwarf star near the Sun. Old One called these times "tribulation." He kept writing in the style of the writers of the Bible, even using their terms—tribulation!

The descendants of Adapa, the biblical Adam, served as kings for the humans. Seth, Enos, Cainan, Malaleel, Jared, Enoch, Methusale, and Lamech are these descendants listed in *Genesis*, Chapter 5. Old One wrote that they are the kings listed on the *Sumerian King's List*.

Lamech had a very beautiful wife, Batanash. The Bible says Lamech and Batanash had a son named Noah. Old One wrote that Enki sum-moned Lamech and Batanash to Eridu. Enki saw Batanash, and desired her. He impregnated Batanash. Noah was the son of Enki and Batanash. (This Enki person needs some counseling.)

According to Old One, Noah was fair skinned. Lamech suspected Noah was the son of one of the gods, the Anunnaki, but Batanash refused to admit she had been impregnated by Enki. Lamech sought advice from his father, Methusale, who told him to accept the word of Batanash. After that, Lamech did not question Batanash again[173].

The Anunnaki who manned the way station on Mars came down to earth and took human wives. These were the "sons of gods who came in unto the daughters of men, and they bare children to them," as it says in *Genesis*. The Nephilim.

Old One told the story of how they taught human women to wear makeup and jewelry. (Remember Kim's Valentine's Day e-mail? The myth was true!) The offspring of the Anunnaki and humans were the Nephilim- -- giants. They were Og, Goliath, and the giant of Gath who had six fingers on each hand and six toes on each foot. The Nephilim[175].

Humans and Anunnaki marrying and having children greatly upset Enlil.

Around the year 10,500 BC, the Anunnaki were aware the next passing of the brown dwarf star would cause the Great Flood, Noah's Flood. Enlil decided to allow the flood to destroy humanity. The Anunnaki kept this information from their creation, the adamu, not warning them. Enlil wanted the flood to wipe out humanity.

However, Enki secretly told his son, Noah, to build a boat that resembled a submarine, giving Noah the dimensions and specific assembly instructions. Enki and Ninhursag collected the DNA, seeds, and eggs of as many life forms as possible. Another of Enki's sons, Ninagal, brought them to Noah's boat. Ninagal then stayed to be the navigator[174].

During the flood, the Anunnaki left the Earth. Some took their human wives and Nephilim offspring with them. Noah and his family survived on the boat. Other humans survived the flood in the North Lands, parts of South America, and parts of Africa.

Old One wrote that after the flood, the gods returned to the Earth. They drained the land in the Middle East and reconstructed their settlements. An Anunnaki architect named Ningishzidda built the Great Pyramid at Giza. (I knew it! The Elohim, the gods, the Anunnaki, built the Great Pyramid at Giza!)

Ningishzidda's face was put on the Sphinx. It wasn't a pharoah's face on the Sphinx, like the Egyptian tour guide had told me. It was the architect god named Ningishzidda, with the body of a lion, the Anunnaki symbol for the Sun.

The gods built a landing strip in Lebanon, a mission control center in Jerusalem, and rebuilt the spaceport in the Sinai Desert[176].

The Nephilim built the city of Jericho, the oldest known city, around 8000 BC. (177)

I was really absorbed in Old One's manuscript, unaware of what was going on around me.

"Did you see my reading glasses? I think I might have left them here."

Magazine Lady's voice startled me. I jumped; the manuscript fell out of my hand.

"Oh, no, um, I didn't see any."

Magazine Lady picked up the manuscript. "Here's your book. I hope you don't mind I moved back a couple seats. Might as well spread out. What is this thing?" She looked it over. "It looks like some ancient manuscript, like parchment paper."

"It's um, well, it is, sort of," I mumbled.

"What's it about?" she asked as she leaned over me.

All of a sudden she wanted to have a conversation?

"It's about the Creation, and some other things." I felt like I was talking to Old One. I sounded like an idiot again.

"Creation of what?" she demanded, still leaning over me.

"The creation of, us, I guess." I wished she would stop leaning over me. She still smelled like coffee.

"Oh, are you a born again?"

She meant a born-again Christian. What a question to ask. She was really nervy!

"I'm not a born again. I mean, I believe in evolution, but, um, I…"

"Evolution?" Magazine Lady interrupted. "It's so obvious, isn't it? We look like monkeys." She stared at me, waiting for a response. I didn't say anything. Why do I let people like her intimidate me?

"You know, humans and chimpanzees have ninety-eight percent of the same DNA." She was persistent. And she was still standing over me.

"Oh, really? I didn't know that, ninety-eight percent. Um, chimpanzees have ninety-eight percent?" I asked.

"Nematodes and humans have seventy-five percent of the same DNA."

I couldn't believe it. The guy behind us said that! He looked like he was a college student. Magazine Lady peered over the seat. She finally stood up straight and stopped leaning over me.

"What?" she asked.

"It's so obvious we descended from nematodes," College Boy spoke again.

"Well, maybe we did," she answered.

"Maybe you did, but I didn't." College Boy was in battle mode.

"And where do you think that you came from?" Magazine Lady battled back.

"I was created." College Boy fired his big gun.

Magazine Lady was glaring at College Boy behind us. I had to end this.

"You're both right. It says in this manuscript."

They both looked at me with puzzled expressions. I couldn't possibly explain this. I had to change the subject.

"I, uh, I didn't see your reading glasses. Sorry."

"I'm thinking I dropped them under the seat." Magazine Lady looked under the seat.

"I don't see them there."

Magazine Lady left. College Boy didn't say anything else. That whole conversation was very awkward and tense. People are very passionate about this creation versus evolution debate. If only they knew—both are correct. There was evolution and creation!

I made a mental note of this conversation. I didn't know nematodes and chimpanzees shared so much of our DNA. When I had time at home, I looked for information on the similarities of human and chimpanzee DNA. The claim that ninety-eight percent of our DNA is shared with chimpanzees is very misleading. We do have ninety-eight percent of the same DNA genomes as chimpanzees. However, eighty percent of the proteins in the human and chimpanzee genomes are different. Proteins are responsible for an organism's anatomical, physiological, and behavioral characteristics. Therefore, a high degree of genetic similarity doesn't mean we are related. We are not related to chimpanzees or nematodes because the proteins that make up our DNA genomes are very different.

A Web site I found listed over one hundred differences between humans and chimpanzees, such as language, brain size, rib cage differences, and so on[178].

After reading this, I became more convinced Old One's story of creation was correct. We do not have a lot in common with chimpanzees. The DNA claim is misleading. It is not obvious we have evolved from monkeys. I wish I had known this when I was on the airplane with Magazine Lady.

To get back on track with Old One's story, I also researched more about Noah's Flood once I was home. According to Old One, it did not reach every part of the Earth. The North Lands and parts of South America and Africa were spared. It affected large parts of the world, with the brunt of the flood occurring in the Middle East.

The cause of the flood was a combination of different occurrences.

There was global warming due to the increase of the Sun's activity. The increase in the Sun's activity was caused by the approach of the brown dwarf star. The global warming caused the Antarctic ice sheets to melt. The melting ice sheets slid and fell into the ocean south and west of the South African Cape, causing a tidal wave[179].

The tidal wave engulfed large parts of the southern globe and the Middle East. At the same time, the gravitational pull of the brown dwarf star caused underwater earthquakes that unleashed tsunamis in various areas. Those were the "fountains of the great deep" mentioned in *Genesis* 7:11. The North Pole and Greenland ice covers had also partially melted, putting more moisture into the atmosphere. This created the deluge from the "windows of heaven" also spoken about in *Genesis* 7:11. [180]

Also, Old One wrote that fragments of comets hit different parts of the Earth, causing further tidal waves and destruction[182].

I spent quite a long time on the Internet investigating the flood. There was a debate on the Internet about whether the flood was localized in the Middle East where Noah was, or whether it was worldwide. Just as before, many anti-Christian/anti-Jewish Web sites tried to prove the Bible incorrect. Interestingly, Moslems were defending the Bible, because the story of the flood is very important in the Quran[183].

The main argument against the flood is that it was localized, in the Middle East only. Geological evidence exists of a devastating flood around the Black Sea area about 5500 BC. Some Web sites claimed this was the flood of the Bible, and it was only in one area.

From what I can tell, that was not Noah's Flood. There were many good arguments *for* a global flood, as told in the Bible.

To begin, ancient stories all over the world tell about a global flood, such as this text from the Esquimaux Native American Tribe of Canada:

> The water having poured over the terrestrial disk,
> human dwellings disappeared…
> The waves traversed the mountains.
> A great wind drove them…
> Men bewailed what happened.
> Uprooted trees floated by in the waves[181].

The following is from *Native Americans in the Carolinas*:

A star fell to the Earth, and rain soon followed.
Days and days of rain quenched the fire[181].

In India, actually Sri Lanka, a story is told of seven temples. Six were buried under the sea. Only one survived, damaged beyond repair. I could go on with flood stories from many peoples: the Aztecs, Chinese, Sumatrans, and many others[181].

The next item I found, in my opinion, proves Old One's story. If Old One is correct, and the melting ice cap slid off Antarctica, then Antarctica would have been ice-free for some time afterwards. There may be some recollection of this among the ancient peoples. And there is.

A group of historians have found an ancient map that confirms this. The map was drawn on a piece of gazelle skin in AD 1513 by a Turkish admiral named Piri Reis. The Turkish admiral had written a series of notes about the map. He had copied the data on the map from a large number of other maps dating back to the fourth century BC or earlier, having found these other maps in the Imperial Library of Constantinople.

The Piri Reis map shows three areas: the western coast of Africa, the eastern coast of South America, and the northern coast of Antarctica—ice free! The Antarctica portion of the map was perfectly detailed. This was three hundred years before Antarctica was discovered in modern times. The American Captain Nathaniel Palmer made the first sighting of Antarctica in 1820! The small peninsula he saw jutting out into the sea was named after him—the Palmer Peninsula.

The Piri Reis map shows the Palmer Peninsula, and another area of Antarctica called Queen Maud Land, ice free! Geological evidence shows the latest date Queen Maud Land and the Palmer Peninsula could have been ice free was about 4000 BC. This area is now covered by an ice cap about one mile thick[184].

Scientists have also determined the last ice-free period for Queen Maud Land and the Palmer Peninsula began between 13,000 BC and 9000 BC. That corresponds to the date Old One gave Noah's Flood—about 10,500 BC.

Who was able to draw a map of Antarctica in 4000 BC or earlier? The Anunnaki, the gods of Sumer, the Elohim. So this information helps to corroborate Old One's dating of the flood and his explanation about the ice cap in Antarctica melting and sliding into the ocean, which caused a tidal wave.

I also tried to find out if any historical data exists about the melting of the ice cover on Greenland. According to Old One, Greenland's ice melted, putting moisture into the atmosphere, helping to bring about the deluge—forty days and nights of rain.

A map was drawn by the Zeno brothers from Venice, Italy in the four-teenth century. It was based on much earlier originals, and shows Greenland as two separate islands. This would only be known if no ice covered Greenland at some time. A recent French polar expedition, using seismic soundings, found a thick ice cap joining what are actually two islands, forming Greenland[185]!

Another part of Old One's story that made sense was about comets hitting the earth at the same time as the flood. If they were partially ice comets, this would have added to the amount of water flooding the planet. A professor at the University of Vienna, named Alexander Toll-man, found evidence to confirm this. If the Earth was hit by a group of comets, there should be splinters of molten rock thrown up by the impacts. These splinters are called "tektites." Professor Tollman claims there is a huge concentration of tektites in sediments laid down around 10,000 BC in different parts of the world! The tektites Professor Tollman found confirm the Earth was hit by seven large comet fragments and many smaller ones[186]!

Professor Tollman also claims part of the ozone layer was destroyed by the comets, exposing the planet to higher levels of radiation and in-creased carbon-14 production. The professor discovered a sudden in-crease in radioactive carbon-14 found in fossilized trees dating back to 10,000 BC[187]! So Old One was right again.

One more item and then I will stop writing about proving Old One's version of the flood. The best estimate of scientists is that around the same time as Old One's flood date, 10,500 BC, the temperature of the earth increased by a worldwide average of twenty degrees in fifty years. That is why the ice caps melted[188].

These catastrophes all occurred because the brown dwarf star passed by the Sun.

After the Flood

You're probably sick of Noah's Flood by now. I'll move ahead!

After Magazine Lady left, I resumed reading the manuscript. Old One continued his story by telling what happened after the flood. He wrote that some humans, animals, and plants had survived in various places around the world. The Anunnaki had preserved the seeds, DNA, and eggs of some plants and animals on Noah's boat. The Anunnaki made the decision to help the remaining humans, showing Noah and his family how to cultivate crops, beginning with the grape. The grape was the first domesticated crop. The gods created domesticated animals from DNA and gave them to humanity[189].

With the next passing of the brown dwarf star, around 7500 BC, the Anunnaki created four civilizations in the river valleys:

1. Tigris and Euphrates Rivers–Sumer (Iraq)

2. Nile River–Egypt

3. Indus River Valley–India

4. Huang He Valley–China [189]

According to Old One, a different god, Anunnaki, was in charge of each civilization. For example, the goddess Inanna was in charge of the Indus River Valley in India. Enki, the doctor, was in charge of the Nile River Valley in Egypt.

I remembered reading a history text written by Herodotus, the Greek historian. Herodotus wrote a history of Egypt around 450 BC, in which he stated there was a time when Egypt was ruled by gods. He really meant that. And, according to Old One, it is true[191].

The Anunnaki also designated the Sinai Desert as a sacred area. That is where their spaceport was located. The Nephilim giants settled in Israel. The Anunnaki taught the humans pottery making, weaving, farming, and many other skills. The mining operations continued in Africa.

Around 3800 BC, Anu, the father in heaven, came down to Earth. He was the supreme ruler of the gods, the Anunnaki. Anu looked just as God is portrayed to be—a wise old man with a long, flowing gray beard. Anu was mature, muscular, and ancient-looking. He had a powerful presence and spoke with a firm, commanding voice[192].

There was great fanfare during Anu's visit to Earth. Anu decided to create a high civilization for the humans to be located in Iraq, between the Tigris and Euphrates Rivers. This was Sumer. The people who lived between the Tigris and Euphrates Rivers were chosen by the Anunnaki to become the first high civilization.

Old One wrote that the Anunnaki called these humans the "black-headed people," because a lot of them had wooly black hair[193].

The black-headed people were taught to build temples called ziggurats. They were instructed to worship the gods, the Elohim, in the temples. The Anunnaki established priests among the black-headed people to be intermediaries between the people and the gods of Sumer. They also established rule by kingship. The kings were usually demi-gods, the sons of a human and an Anunnaki. The people of Sumer were taught how to write, how to heal the sick, and were given a code of law. Most of the "firsts" of civilization came from Sumer—given to the black-headed people by the Anunnaki[194].

For a time the gods were pleased; then trouble arose among them. The disagreements and rivalry between Enki and Enlil developed into warfare among their descendants. They battled each other across the globe. Old One wrote the stories in detail. They were rather boring; petty jealousies erupted into personal challenges. Old One even described aerial battles between the gods.

The horrible part for us is that Marduk, the son of Enki, began using human armies to take over other gods' territories. This resulted in the War of the Kings around the year 2000 BC. Old One wrote that Sodom and Gomorrah were destroyed by two of the gods who used nuclear-type weapons fired from an aircraft. The same two gods also destroyed the spaceport in the Sinai Desert to keep it from falling into the hands of Marduk[195].

That's exactly what Becky's e-mail had said. She found plenty of evidence Sodom and Gomorrah and the spaceport in the Sinai Desert were destroyed by nuclear-type weapons.

The destruction of the spaceport resulted in a radiation cloud that destroyed Sumer. The gods fled the area, some heading to the Americas and beginning gold mining operations there. They founded the Aztec, Mayan, and Incan civilizations and built the ziggurats in Mexico and South America. That is why the architecture of ancient Central America resembled the architecture of ancient Egypt and the Middle East[196].

During the War of the Kings, Enlil recruited Abraham to guard the spaceport in the Sinai Desert. Abraham successfully prevented Marduk's forces from entering that area of the Sinai Desert. As a reward, Enlil promised Abraham his descendants would inherit the land from the Nile River to the Euphrates River. Abraham's descendants are the Jews and the Arabs. That is where they live today!

Moses

Old One wrote that after the War of the Kings, Enlil left his city, Nippur, and went to live in the mountains of Southern Arabia. He did not go to the Sinai Desert because it was contaminated. When Enlil was in Nippur, he was called by many names: "King of Lands," "King of Heaven and Earth," "Lord of the Wind," and "Lord of the Command." However, he had one more name that became very important. It was derived from his dwelling in Nippur, his temple, called Ekur, meaning the "House of the Mountain." Ekur was a lofty structure, built in imitation of a mountain, with a sacred shrine to Enlil at the top. So Enlil was also called the "Lord of the Mountain." Remember that name. It will become important soon[197,199].

After the War of the Kings, Enlil could no longer occupy his "House of the Mountain" because of radiation contamination. Babylon and other areas of the Middle East were barred to him because of Marduk's supremacy. So Enlil went to Southern Arabia and began to plot his return to power.

In an attempt to bring peace, Marduk rebuilt the temple to Enlil at Nippur in 1953 BC, but Enlil refused to return[200].

According to Old One, the next important event was the birth of Moses in Egypt around 1500 BC. Moses was part Egyptian and part Hebrew. He was a descendant by some generations of the Hebrew Joseph's daughter (Joseph was the guy with the "coat of many colors") and an Egyptian Pharoah. That is why he was raised in the court of the Pharoah, and why he cared about the Hebrew slaves in Egypt[202].

In *Exodus* 2:11-15 of the Bible, Moses killed an Egyptian who was beating a Hebrew slave and as a result had to flee from Egypt. Old One wrote that Moses fled Egypt because he was a follower of the Aten cult. The Aten cult was a new religion that only recognized one God, who had no shape or form. The Aten cult was forced upon the Egyptians by the Pharoah Amenhotep IV. The Egyptians, led by their priests, rebelled against the followers of Aten, forcing Moses to flee. He fled to the land of Midian, which is in Saudia Arabia[207,208].

In Midian, Moses married Zipporah, the daughter of Jethro. This Jethro was a descendant of Ishmael, the son of Abraham.

According to Old One, Moses had a flock of sheep he would take to graze on a mountain called Jabal Al Lawz, near Midian[203]. While Moses was grazing his sheep, he met Enlil, the Anunnaki, on the mountain. When they met, Enlil said something strange. Moses knew Enlil was a god of Sumer. He asked Enlil which god he was. Enlil replied: "I am who am: and I appeared unto Abraham, unto Isaac, and unto Jacob as El Shaddai, but by my name 'I am who am,' I was not known to them." This quote from Enlil is also in the Torah—*Exodus* 3:5 and *Exodus* 3:14. It is in my Bible also. God said "I am who am." My Bible leaves out the word "El Shaddai." I have to say this. Popeye said a similar thing to Brutus, or was it Olive Oil? "I am who I am and that's all that I am–I'm Popeye the sailor man."

If I were at home, my grandmother would yell at me for saying that. I guess that would be considered disrespectful. You're right, grandma. Sorry.

"I am who am." The Hebrew word that means "I am who am" is "Yahweh." According to Old One, from that time until now, Enlil was known as Yahweh by the Hebrews.

Enlil wanted to keep his identity a secret from the Hebrews. However, he gave one clue to Moses. "El Shaddai." El Shaddai means "god of the mountain." This refers to Enlil's ziggurat in Nippur—Ekur. Enlil was the god of that ziggurat, the "mountain" ziggurat.

There also is a Sumerian hymn to Enlil that refers to him as a mountain. The words to the hymn are: "Without Enlil, the Great Mountain, no cities would be built, no settlements founded[198]."

Remember the Arameans? They were defeated in the mountains by the Israelites because the God of the Israelites, Yahweh, was the God of the Mountains.

So, Enlil was Yahweh, according to this Book of The Truth.

Old One went through the whole story of Moses: the plagues of Egypt, the Exodus of the Hebrews, and the crossing of the Gulf of Aqaba. Old One wrote that the Hebrews crossed the Gulf of Aqaba, not the Red Sea. I was always taught they crossed the Red Sea, which God parted for them[209].

Old One gave the location of the crossing on the Gulf of Aqaba. He said on the Egyptian side, the left bank, was the Egyptian fortress of Pi-hahiroth. On the Saudi Arabian side was the village of Baal-Zephon, in Midian[211].

As soon as the Hebrews crossed the Gulf of Aqaba, they were attacked by the people of Elim. It says this in *Exodus* 17:8 of the Bible. Elim is near Baal-Zephon, by the Gulf of Aqaba.

After the battle, Moses led the Israelites further south to the mountain called Jabal Al Lawz, where they stayed with Enlil/Yahweh[210].

Old One told the story of the Ten Commandments. Enlil based the commandments on Egyptian writings such as the Egyptian *Book of the Dead*.

According to Old One, Enlil came and went in a flying machine called a Kabod, that caused a lot of smoke and fumes. Because of this, the top of the mountain at Jabal Al Lawz was blackened. Old One wrote that Moses suffered radiation burns on his face from getting too close to the Kabod. It says this in *Exodus* 34:30: "When Aaron and the Israelites saw Moses, the skin of his face was shining[204]."

At one point, Moses stayed in the mountains with Enlil for many days. When he returned, the Israelites had made a golden calf, the symbol of another god. Enlil commanded Moses to kill those who had done this. Moses and the Israelite priests, the Levites, killed over three thousand Israelites! Enlil was a jealous god[205].

Enlil kept the Israelites in Saudi Arabia for forty years to increase their numbers, to make them worship only Enlil, and to train them for the conquest of the Nephilim in Canaan. Enlil wanted to destroy the seed of Enki with the seed of Eve, as he had promised in the Garden of Eden. The Nephilim were the seed of Enki—the descendants of Anunnaki and humans. The Hebrews were the seed of Eve.

Moses died before the conquest of Canaan began. His body was put in a sepulchre by Enlil. Then Michael, the "messenger" of Enlil, took the body to the heavens where he was resurrected[201]!

That was quite a story. For the most part, it followed the Bible, but had some new twists and additional information. So I had to see what could be proven or corroborated.

At home once again, I went to the Internet. As with every other major event in the Bible, anti-Christian and anti-Jewish Web sites were trying to prove Moses did not exist, the Exodus never happened, and the story of the Ten Commandments was made up.

And, once again, interestingly, Moslems were defending the Bible story. Moses is a great prophet in Islam.

The first proof I found was archaeological evidence that the Red Sea crossing actually took place on the Gulf of Aqaba—not the Red Sea. In 1978, Israeli soldiers found a seventeen-foot-tall red granite column on Nuweiba Beach, which is on the Gulf of Aqaba. A matching column was found on the other side of the Gulf, directly across from Nuweiba Beach. The columns had the Hebrew words for Egypt, death, water, pharaoh, Yahweh, and Solomon. It is believed King Solomon had these pillars erected to commemorate the Gulf of Aqaba crossing by the Hebrews[212]. I found out the columns are even mentioned in the Bible, *Isaiah* 19:19: "In that day there will be an altar to the Lord in the midst of the land of Egypt, and a pillar to the Lord at its border."

The Bible concurs with the Gulf of Aqaba crossing. According to *Exodus* 3:18, the Israelites first fled through the "wilderness of the Red Sea," an area in the northern Sinai Desert. Next, the Bible says God told Moses to turn south. Old One wrote when they turned south, they came to a canyon area on the Gulf of Aqaba in which they were trapped. To the north were high mountains and the Egyptian fortress of Pi-hahiroth. To the south were cliffs that came down to the sea. In front of them was the Gulf of Aqaba. Behind them were the Egyptian soldiers and their chariots.

Josephus wrote in his *Antiquities of the Jews*: "For there was on each side a ridge of mountains that terminated at the sea, which were impassable by reason of their roughness, and obstructed their flight[213]."

Exodus 14:3 says the Israelites "became entangled in the land, the wilderness hath shut them in."

The beach at Nuweiba on the Gulf of Aqaba fits these descriptions perfectly. According to a Web site by Anthony Grigor-Scott[210], the Israeli soldiers also made another discovery at Nuweiba Beach. Numerous chariot wheels, plus human and horse bones, are under the water.

"The Lord looked unto the host of the Egyptians through the pillar of fire and of the cloud, and troubled the host of the Egyptians, clogging their chariot wheels, that they drove heavily and broke…The Egyptians said let us flee, for the Lord fights for them." (*Exodus* 14:23-28)

According to the Web site, the wheels found were four, six, and eight-spoke chariot wheels, identified by the Department of Antiquities in Cairo as belonging to the Eighteenth Dynasty. The Eighteenth Dynasty was in the time of Moses.

Even more amazingly, a massive sand bar, almost a mile wide, goes across the Gulf of Aqaba from Nuweiba Beach. It slopes gently at six degrees until midway across the Gulf, where it is nine hundred feet below sea level. Then it rises to the other shore at the same angle. The rest of the Gulf is over three thousand to five thousand feet deep. This would have been the best place to part the waters of the Gulf. Old One wrote that Enlil/Yahweh parted the water using wind made by his Kabod[201]. The Bible says God caused a great east wind to blow the waters back.

So, according to this evidence, the crossing occurred. However, it was across the Gulf of Aqaba, which is a branch of the Red Sea forming part of the border between Egypt and Saudia Arabia.

Next, Old One's manuscript said Mt. Sinai was actually the mountain Jabal al Lawz, near Midian, Saudi Arabia.

Exodus 2:15 says "Moses fled from the face of the Pharaoh and dwelt in the land of Midian." Midian is in Saudi Arabia. "And she (Ziporrah) bore him a son, and he called his name Gershom; for he said I have been a stranger in a foreign land." (*Exodus* 2:22) Moses was saying he was in a foreign land. Therefore, he could not have been in the Sinai Desert, which was part of Egypt. Moses was in Midian, on the eastern side of the Gulf of Aqaba. Today, Midian is part of Saudi Arabia; it has never been part of Egypt[214].

The Bible says the Lord appeared to Moses in the "wilderness of Mount Sinai" (not on Mount Sinai) in *Acts* 7:29-30. Josephus said Mt. Sinai "was the highest of mountains in the city of Midian." Jabal al Lawz, the mountain Old One referred to, is the highest mountain in Midian, in South Arabia. Philo, the Greek/Jewish philosopher from Alexandria, wrote Mt. Sinai was located east of the Sinai Desert, and south of Palestine. That location could be Midian, where Jabal al Lawz is located. So it appears the mountain where Moses met Enlil/Yahweh, and then led the Israelites to, was actually in Saudi Arabia. Jabal al Lawz, Saudi Arabia; not Mt. Sinai in the Sinai Desert[215].

The peak of Jabal al Lawz is still today burned black at the top of the mountain, caused by Enlil/Yahweh's Kabod landing and taking off[216].

In *Exodus* 19:18, the mountain is described as "altogether covered in smoke, for the Lord descended upon it in fire; its smoke ascended like that of a furnace." The Saudis will not permit tourists onto the mountain top to confirm the blackened peaks. However, they were confirmed by U.S. government satellite photos[216].

The Bible also gives an accounting of the Israelites camping at the base of the mountain. Thousands of acres spread from the base of the mountain, while being clearly visible from the mountain top. This could be where the Israelites camped.

When the Israelites arrived at the base of Jabal al Lawz, they had no water to drink. "The Lord said to Moses, go before the elders, and take your rod in your hand…and you shall strike the rock and water shall come out of it." (I *Corinthians* 10:4)

That rock is a prominent landmark standing sixty feet above the western foothills of Jabal al Lawz. It is split enough for a man to pass through. Erosion markings show water once flowed through the rock to the plain below!

Exodus 24:4 continues to support the archaeological evidence. "And Moses built an altar under the hill, and twelve pillars, according to the twelve tribes of Israel."

At the eastern foot of Jabal al Lawz are the remnants of an altar of unhewn stones. Within the stones is a semicircle of the remains of twelve white granite pillars!

Researchers believe they have found the area where the altar to the golden calf was built. In addition, they have found prepared ground which may be the place where the animals were corralled. Local people call Jabal al Lawz "The Mountain of Moses[216]."

In my opinion, Jabal al Lawz is the mountain where Moses met Enlil/Yahweh, and where he received the Ten Commandments. Jabal al Lawz, in Midian, Saudi Arabia.

Old One was correct so far about everything. The next point he made about Moses is when he died, Enlil/Yahweh personally interred him in a sepulcher. Then Michael, the messenger of Enlil/Yahweh, took the body to heaven, and Moses was resurrected. In the Bible, in *Jude* 1:9, it says: "Yet Michael the archangel, when contending with the devil he disputed about the body of Moses, durst not bring against him a railing accusation, but said, the Lord rebuke thee."

I think this means Michael took the body of Moses. The remains of Moses have never been found[217].

The name Michael comes from the word Micah, which means "one who is like unto God." This God probably refers to Enlil, so Michael was like Enlil. He was some type of Anunnaki. The Anunnaki had resurrected gods, according to ancient texts.

I know Moses was seen again about 1,400 years later at the Transfiguration of Jesus. So at least for now, I am going to believe Old One. He's been right about everything else.

An important part of the story of Moses concerns the writing of the Torah. Old One explained some interesting facts about its origin.

The Torah became the first five books of the Old Testament. I was taught that Yahweh had dictated the Torah to Moses on Mt. Sinai. Old One claimed part of the Torah was written by Moses and Enlil/Yahweh on Jabal al Lawz. Part of it was copied from the Babylonian and Sumerian sacred texts, during the Babylonian captivity of the Jews. Ricky had said the same thing when I was in Babylon. I did some of my own research on this claim.

In the Torah (*Genesis* 36) is an extensive list of the kings of Edom, some of whom reigned *after* the death of Moses. Moses could not have written about the kings of Edom who reigned after his death.

A story in *Genesis* 14:14 tells of Abraham rescuing Lot in the city of "Dan." That city was not called "Dan" until long after Moses died. During Moses' lifetime, it was called "Laish." Moses could not have written about the city of "Dan."

I think Old One was correct again. Moses only wrote part of the Torah. Some of it came from Babylon and probably Sumer. This could also explain why God had different names in different parts. I wish I had known all of this when I was in Iraq. I would have loved to discuss this with Ricky[217,218].

The last point Old One made is about what Enlil did to Enki in the Torah. Enlil portrayed Enki as a snake, the devil. Enki tempted Eve in the Garden of Eden. The temptation was the ability to reproduce, the Tree of Knowledge. So for all time, Enki became the evil snake, the devil.

When I looked into this, I found out Enki's "symbol" was the snake. He was pictured often wearing a headdress that resembles a snake[206,219], kind of like the headdress Yaser Arafat, the former Palestinian leader, would wear sometimes. In fact, some Iraqis used to wear that type of head covering, making their heads look like snakes. I wonder if there is some connection to Enki?

Aunt Sophia

The long flight to New York was finally over! We touched down at LaGuardia Airport at 12:08 P.M. All I could think was—I'm HUNGRY. It was lunch time and I was STARVED. Two hours remained until my connecting flight to Washington, D.C.. Looking out of the window, I noted the plethora of activity: planes taking off, planes taxiing, luggage handlers driving back and forth. It was so great to be back in America!

I exited the airplane. I had made it. America! At the gate, I looked around. It was so crowded. People were coming and going—everyone was in a hurry. There were children in strollers, women in regular clothes, jeans, skirts, and short pants, and men in suits. I was home! It was so great. Then a face came into focus; someone I know. Kim, my sister! She must have gotten the e-mail of my flight itinerary. She ran and hugged me. It was *so* great to see her. Kim's hair was longer, and I noticed the oversized diamond on her hand.

"Come on, we'll get lunch real quick. I have to go back to work. I tried to get off this afternoon but I have a presentation." Kim always used to boss me around. Some things will never change. "Let's get bagels."

A bagel! I hadn't had a bagel for—I couldn't remember the last time. We ordered cheese bagels with extra cream cheese. Then we both scraped off the extra cream cheese and didn't eat it. Must be genetic.

Kim seemed as if she wanted to say something, but was holding back. We talked about our sister June, June's husband, mom and dad, Kim's dog, and Kim's fiancée. They had set a date for their wedding—October 9. I'm going to be in a wedding! I love weddings. A fall wedding in New

York. Kim still seemed to be holding something back. Finally she took my hand and glanced away before beginning.

"I, um, (we all say "um" frequently in my family) have something to tell you. I didn't know whether I should tell you now or not. But I guess I should." She stopped and took a deep breath, her eyes sad.

"June called me this morning. It's Aunt Sophia. She, um, she passed away yesterday, in the morning. They think she had a stroke in her sleep, and they couldn't wake her. She died a little while later."

Kim stared at me, waiting for a reaction. Aunt Sophia was my favorite aunt. She's the one who gave to me the Orthodox Bible when I was ten years old. Tears welled up in my eyes. I wanted to cry, but held it in. Kim gripped my hand tightly.

"I wanted to see her again." My voice was cracking.

"I know. I'm so sorry, Joy."

"Was she still in the Rest Time Nursing Home?" I asked. Aunt Sophia had been in a nursing home in Ohio.

"Yes, Joy, she was."

"Then she died alone. No one should die alone," I said quietly.

"The funeral is on Saturday," Kim said gently.

I had to go to the funeral. I wanted to see Aunt Sophia laid to rest. I decided when I got home, I was going to call my sister, June, in Pittsburgh. Maybe June was going to the funeral. I could drive there the next day, and go to Ohio from her house.

Life is so fickle. My happiness at being home turned to depression. Aunt Sophia had died. Kim couldn't even stay to spend time with me, and I wouldn't see her again until her wedding. Sadness weighed heavily on me as I said my goodbyes to my sister.

Boarding the plane, I felt down, depressed, and questions were popping into my head. Is there life after death, reincarnation, do we have souls? Where is Aunt Sophia now? Lisa believes we go to another dimension. Ricky said heaven is up in the sky. The Hebrews believed the soul stays around the body for three days after death.

I remembered a story I had read in a magazine about a near death experience. A doctor, I think his name was Dr. Melvin Morse (I remembered his name because of Morse code), interviewed an eleven-year-old boy who went into cardiac arrest in the lobby of a hospital. The boy remembered a sinking feeling, "like when you go over a bump in a car and your stomach drops out from under you." He heard a whooshing sound and people talking. Then, he was floating on the ceiling, looking down at his body. He heard a nurse say, "I wish we didn't have to do this." He then saw a nurse put some grease on his body as she handed paddles to the doctor. The paddles were placed on his body, and when the doctor pressed the button, "I was suddenly back in my body looking up at the doctor." Nurses who were present recounted that he opened his eyes and said, "That was really weird, I was floating above my body and was sucked back into myself[220]."

That story stayed with me. It could be evidence something continues to exist after our bodies die. Maybe Aunt Sophia didn't just cease to exist. It gave me some comfort.

The Hebrews

Back on the airplane, I sat quietly, letting my sorrow wash over me. I looked out the window at the rain beginning to fall. I hadn't seen rain for awhile. It matched my mood. A strange-looking man sat in the aisle seat next to me, balding on top, with a ponytail in the back. The strange man had a worn-out suit on, a tie, and no socks! Strange Man looked at me and smiled, saying "Hi." I responded out of politeness but didn't feel like talking, so I picked up Old One's manuscript. I started reading again.

The section I had reached now discussed the Hebrew conquest of Canaan.

When Moses died, a man named Joshua became the new leader of the Israelites. He carried out Enlil/Yahweh's command to wipe out the seed of Enki, the Nephilim. The Nephilim had built the city of Jericho in Canaan and settled in other areas of Canaan. (The present day boundaries of Israel comprise a lot of ancient Canaan.) *The wars to conquer Canaan were genocidal wars. Joshua and the Hebrews did not just conquer the Nephilim, they wiped them out. In Jericho, they slaughtered everyone except a prostitute who was spared because she had helped two Hebrew spies.*

A description of this event is also found in the Biblical book of *Joshua* 6:21: "And they utterly destroyed all that was in the city, both man and woman, young and old, and ox and sheep, and ass, with the edge of the sword."

Old One wrote Enlil/Yahweh helped with the battle by causing the walls of Jericho to fall down.

The next city the Israelites attacked was called Ai. It had a population of twelve thousand. All of the people of Ai were butchered, and the city was burned to the ground. Enlil was having his revenge on the seed of Enki[221].

The savage genocide continued for city after city. The Hebrews killed all of the Nephilim giants: King Og who had a bed that was eighteen feet long, and the Giant of Gath who had six fingers on each hand and six toes on each foot. Eventually, David slew the thirteen-foot, six-inch Goliath, and the Hebrews killed many others.

Joshua 10:40 recounts a similar story. "So Joshua killed all in the country of the hills and of the south and of the valleys, and of the springs, and all their kings: he left none remaining, but utterly destroyed all that breathed, as the Lord God of Israel commanded."

Many people have trouble reconciling this genocidal, savage God Yahweh of the Old Testament with the merciful God Jesus spoke of in the New Testament. In the Old Testament, God was a vengeful Anunnaki. I hoped Old One would explain who the merciful God of Jesus is in the New Testament.

Old One continued with stories of King David and King Solomon. Enlil/Yahweh became very angry with the Israelites because they continued to worship other gods. Remember Enlil/Yahweh's first commandment: "No other gods before me." *I Kings* 11:45 says: "When Solomon grew old, his wives swayed his heart to other gods; and his heart was not wholly with Yahweh, his God...Solomon became a follower of Astarte, the goddess of the Sidonians."

Enlil/Yahweh was angry with the Israelites. So he allowed the Assyrians to conquer and destroy the northern part of Israel. The Assyrians killed some and assimilated others. These became the "ten lost tribes" of Israel. Many were taken to Persia[223]. After this, only two tribes remained near Jerusalem, the tribes of Judah and Benjamin. They were forced to pay tribute to the Assyrian king. In 701 BC, the Israelite King Hezekiah refused to pay tribute to the Assyrian King Sennacherib. When the Assyrians surrounded Jerusalem and threatened to destroy the city, King Hezekiah cried out to Enlil/Yahweh. During the night, Enlil/Yahweh killed all of the Assyrians in their encampment—185,000 of them!

This story is also told in the Bible, in *Isaiah* 37:36-37: "The angel of the Lord went forth, and smote the camp of the Assyrians a hundred and four score and five thousands: and when they arose early in the morning, behold, they were all dead corpses."

Even after Enlil/Yahweh saved Jerusalem, the son of Hezekiah, whose name was Manasseh, built an altar to the god Baal in the temple in Jerusalem around the year 650 BC.

Manasseh's grandson, Josiah, cleansed the temple and destroyed the statues of all other gods. He restored the temple for Enlil/Yahweh, but it was too late! Enlil/Yahweh could not forgive what Manasseh had done. In 586 BC, he allowed the King of Babylon, Nebuchadnezzar, to conquer Jerusalem and take the Israelites to Babylon. They spent seventy years in captivity in Babylon as their punishment[222].

It was in Babylon they finished writing the Torah and were no longer permitted to say or write the name Yahweh.

The Prophets

Old One wrote that right before the capture of the Israelites by Nebuchadnezzar, Enlil/Yahweh left the Earth. Ancient Babylonian texts called the *Harran Inscriptions* agree, stating that Yahweh became angry with his city, Jerusalem, and caused Nebuchadnezzar and the Babylonians to conquer it. The Babylonians destroyed the temple of Yahweh, and captured the Israelites. The *Harran* texts say prior to the capture, Yahweh left the Earth, in a year calculated to be 597 BC, and the god Sin left his temple in Harran in the same year. Sin returned in a year calculated to be 556 BC. They do not say whether Yahweh returned. Where did Yahweh and Sin go? My guess is Planet X. I'm also guessing Yahweh returned for the rebuilding of the temple in Jerusalem and for the birth of Jesus[224].

Enlil was disgusted with humanity. He had succeeded in wiping out the Nephilim, but he couldn't keep his chosen people, the Hebrews, from worshipping other gods and breaking the other commandments. Enlil/Yahweh considered humanity to be sinners. His definition of a sinner was anyone who did not worship him as the supreme god. (Remember Soddom and Gomorrah's sin!)

When Enlil left, Enki created prophets and enlightened beings in the various human cultures. Some of these were Lao Tsu, Buddha, Confucius, and Zoroaster. They taught about the Creator of All. For the first time, humans did not have to worship Anunnakis. This time, between 600 BC and the birth of Jesus, was a period of enlightenment[225].

The story continued. To understand Jesus, Old One wrote, we should first study the prophecies of the Israelites. He began quoting some of the prophecies about the Messiah. The first was *Isaiah* 7:14 written in 758 BC:

"Therefore the Lord Himself will give you a sign: Behold, the *almah* shall conceive and bear a son, and shall call his name Immanuel." Old One felt that it was necessary to explain the word *almah*, writing that an *almah* is a temple maiden. Mary, the mother of Jesus, was a temple maiden. Old One wrote that in *all* cases, temple maidens were virgins. He did not elaborate[226,227].

The Hebrews referred to Enlil/Yahweh as "the Lord." "Immanuel" means "the most high is with us." This prophecy meant that Enlil/Yahweh will give the Hebrews a sign. The sign is a temple maiden conceiving and bearing a son, and he will be called "Immanuel," which means "the most high is with us."

But a sign of what? The manuscript did not say. The Isaiah prophecy in the Bible is part of a discussion where the Lord tells Isaiah the "House of David," meaning the Hebrews, will survive against its enemies. The only logical conclusion is that Jesus would be a sign the Hebrews would survive because Enlil/Yahweh, "the most high," is with them[228].

Next, Old One quoted *Isaiah* 11:1 and 11:10, written in 713 BC. "And there shall come forth a shoot out of the stem of Jesse, and a branch from his roots shall bear fruit…And in that day there shall stand for an ensign of the people; to it shall the Gentiles seek: and his rest shall be glorious."

Jesus will come from the House of David, and the Gentiles will follow Him. At first I was confused, but then I remembered from the "dueling genealogies" that Jesse was the father of David. Also, an ensign is a signal or a sign. So, Jesus is a sign again.

"[F]or the Earth shall be full of the knowledge of the Lord." (*Isaiah* 11:9) So, Jesus, the sign, was going to spread the knowledge of Yahweh. And in *Luke* 2:34-35, "This child is destined to cause the falling and rising of many in Israel, and to be a sign that will be spoken against…"

Notice it says "falling" first—Israel will fall. Then it says "rising"— Israel will rise. I think this quote also means Jesus is a sign that Israel, the House of David, will survive.

The Quran also says in *Sura* 23:50 that Jesus and His mother, Mary, are a sign from God.

So Jesus is a sign. A sign the House of David will survive.

The next prophecy was recorded in *Isaiah* 40:3, written in 712 BC. "The voice of him that crieth in the wilderness, prepare ye the way of the Lord."

Old One wrote this was the prophecy about John the Baptist preparing the way for Jesus. I guess John the Baptist was the "voice of him that crieth in the wilderness."

The location of Jesus' birth was another fact prophesied about in the Old Testament, in *Micah* 5:2. "The ruler of Israel…would come out of Bethlehem."

Then Old One wrote about the two greatest prophecies of all time (in my opinion). The first is *Daniel* 9:25: "Know, therefore and understand, that from the going forth of the commandment to restore and to build Jerusalem unto the Messiah the Prince shall be seven weeks, and three-score and two weeks" (sixty-nine weeks).

This was a prediction of the exact date Jesus would ride into Jerusalem and the people would proclaim Him to be the Messiah. Palm Sunday! Daniel was one of the Hebrews captured by Nebuchadnezzar in 586 BC and taken back to Babylon when Jerusalem was destroyed. In 445 BC, another emperor, named Artaxerxes Longimanus, issued an edict to re-build Jerusalem. Exactly 483 years later, using the Jewish year of 360 days, Jesus rode into Jerusalem and was publicly proclaimed to be the Messiah. That was in AD 32, the first Palm Sunday.

According to biblical scholars, the "weeks" in Daniel's prophecy meant years. I don't know how they determined that, but if you substitute weeks for years, Daniel hit the date exactly—483 years. They compute the 483 years by taking seven weeks plus three score (a score is twenty so three score is sixty) plus two weeks equals sixty-nine weeks. There are seven days in a week, so sixty nine multiplied by seven days is 483. The scholars say that is 483 years.

That's confusing. The prophets always spoke in riddles, for some sadistic reason. Anyway, Daniel predicted Palm Sunday—exactly—almost six hundred years before it happened.

Next Daniel said: "And *after* threescore and two weeks shall the Messiah be cut off, but not for Himself: and the *people* of the *Prince* shall destroy the city and the sanctuary." (*Daniel* 9:26, emphasis mine)

This prediction meant the Messiah would be killed in AD 32. He would be "cut off" (killed) but not for Himself (resurrected), and *after* AD 32, Jerusalem would be destroyed again.

Jesus was crucified and resurrected in AD 32. The Romans destroyed Jerusalem and the temple (the sanctuary) in AD 70. Jesus' church, the Christian Church, came to be centered in Rome, so the Romans became His *people*. The dating is a little confusing. The "three score and two weeks" is sixty two multiplied by seven, equaling 434. That would mean 434 years. This is forty-nine years less than the first prediction. It took forty-nine years to rebuild the temple in Jerusalem. So the second prophecy counted from the date that the temple was rebuilt. It was 434 years from the completion of the temple until Jesus died and was resurrected. Daniel had the dates correct again[229,230].

What I learned from the prophets were these things:

1. Jesus would be born from a temple maiden, an *almah*. *Almahs* are always virgins.

2. The birth of Jesus is a sign. I think it is a sign the House of David will survive, even though Enlil/Yahweh had left the Earth and was not here to take care of his people.

3. Jesus would be born in Bethlehem. John the Baptist would prepare the way.

4. Jesus would spread the knowledge about Yahweh all over the Earth.

5. Jesus would be killed and resurrected. The Gentiles would follow Him. The Romans would destroy Jerusalem. The Romans would become His people.

The Messiah

Old One was right; studying the prophecies gave some insight into Jesus. He wrote it was Gabriel, the messenger of Enlil, who told the prophets what would happen, and Jesus made every effort to comply with the prophecies.

He named many other prophecies Jesus fulfilled, almost three hundred altogether. Many were about the crucifixion and resurrection. In my opinion, there is little doubt Jesus was the Messiah of the prophets[231].

Next, the manuscript addressed the birth of Jesus. Mary was specifically bred to be the mother of the Messiah. Her father was an angel, an Anunnaki. Her mother, Anna, had met the angel in her garden while her husband was in the wilderness. Mary was raised in the temple and was fed by an "angel," an Anunnaki. She conceived Jesus artificially and was told to *call* her baby Immanuel, which means "the most high is with us." Then an "angel" appeared to Mary's husband, Joseph. He told Joseph to *name* the baby Yahoshu, which means "Yahweh saves." That is because Jesus was a sign from Yahweh that He would save His people.

Old One made a claim I could not verify. He wrote Jesus was Yahweh's son. However, I can't dispute it either. Jesus spoke of His father in heaven. In my opinion, when the ancients spoke of heaven, they meant the home of the Anunnaki, the planet that revolves around the brown dwarf star. Was Jesus speaking of Enlil/Yahweh who had left the Earth? Jesus also said: "When you see Me, you are seeing the One who sent Me." (*John* 12:45) According to the prophets, Yahweh sent Jesus as a sign. Yahweh sent Jesus; therefore, Jesus was his son?

Here's what Old One wrote about the early years of Jesus. My research and references about each point are at the end of the outline.

1. In the year 7 BC, King Herod was ordered by the Romans to take a census in Israel. The census was done in the Jewish pattern; that is, numbering by tribe. That is why Joseph had to go to Bethlehem and Jesus was born there in 4 BC, in the month of October.

2. The "Star of Bethlehem" was a rare alignment of Earth, Jupiter, and Saturn. The alignments appeared three times during that year. It was only visible at dawn, and it could be seen over Bethlehem if traveling south from Jerusalem. There was also a comet involved.

3. The "Star of Bethlehem" was visible in the constellation Pisces. The ancient symbol for Pisces was the fish. The "Age of Pisces" began about that time. That is why the Christian symbol for Jesus is a fish. (It is not because He was a "fisher of men" like I was taught in Bible school).

4. The story of the three Magi is true. They came to Bethlehem because of the conjunction of the three planets.

5. There was a messenger of Enlil/Yahweh at the birth (an angel). *Shepherds did come from the hills to see the baby. The Magi brought gold for a king, incense for a god, and myrrh for a man.*

6. Herod sent soldiers to kill all infants in Bethlehem. The city of Bethlehem was a very small suburb of Jerusalem. There were only a few infants in the town. Joseph was warned by (an angel) *a messenger of Enlil/Yahweh the soldiers were coming. He fled to Egypt with Mary and Jesus. Mary's cousin, Elizabeth, was also warned. She fled to the wilderness with her baby, John the Baptist. Other families fled Bethlehem before the soldiers came. The husband of Elizabeth, whose name was Zecharias, was killed by Herod's soldiers because he would not reveal where they had fled to.*

7. Joseph kept Jesus in Egypt until Herod's death and the end of a revolt by the Hebrews around Jerusalem. Then He returned to Israel. Joseph did not take Jesus back to Bethlehem. Joseph went north to the area called Galilee and settled in a small town called Nazareth.

8. To avoid being pledged in a marriage, Jesus left Israel with a trade caravan and went to the East at the age of thirteen. While in the East, He was taught by Hindu priests and studied Buddhism. He did not return to Israel until his twenty-ninth year.

I want to stop here and share some information I had found later at home on these eight points about the Messiah.

The census: It is debated if there was a census in Israel at the time of Jesus' birth. Josephus recorded in the *Antiquities of the Jews* that Caesar Augustus was furious with Herod in 8 BC and threatened to treat him as a subject instead of a friend. Some scholars believe this meant Herod's kingdom would now be subject to taxes, and a census was ordered. It took a couple of years to organize the census. That is why Joseph and Mary had to report to Bethlehem at the time of Jesus' birth.

John Malalas, a historian of Antioch, Syria, in AD 500, wrote that a census was taken of all the Earth under the Romans, registered by the Roman Senator Attalus in 5 BC. Another Roman historian, Tertullian, records a census taken in Judea by Sentius Saturninus. Sentius Saturninus was the legate of Syria from 9 BC to 6 BC.

In the Bible, Luke writes that a census took place while Sulpicius Quirinius was the governor of Syria. (*Luke* 2:2) This has caused a lot of confusion. Sulpicius Quirinius was the governor of Syria in AD 6 and AD 7. For a long time, this was used to discredit Luke and the Bethlehem story. Some people still use this today to discredit Luke. In 1912, a fragmentary inscription was found at Antioch that explained this discrepancy. It described the Roman conquest of Syria by Quirinius from 10 BC to 7 BC. In 7 BC, Quirinius established a Roman seat of government around Syria. The Roman province of Syria included Judea. Quirinius probably would have taken a census, as described by Tertullian, as part of the process of establishing a Roman seat of government. He later became the governor in AD 6. Luke was probably correct and a census was taken by Quirinius when he conquered Syria.

So Tertullian, Josephus, the Antioch fragment, John Malalas, and Luke all say there was a census! (I guess Josephus implies, not says, there was a census.) I could not find an argument that disproved it[232].

The Star of Bethlehem: On December 17, 1603, the German astronomer, Johannes Kepler, observed the conjunction of the planets of Saturn and Jupiter in the constellation Pisces. He calculated the same conjunction occurred in 7 BC, and occurs every 805 years.

In the Sumerian city of Sippar, ancient clay tablets were found in 1925, dating back thousands of years. One tablet recorded the position of Saturn and Jupiter, converged in Pisces over a five-month period in 7 BC. The first was on May 7, the second on September 15, and the third on October 6. This was followed by a near conjunction of Mars, Jupiter, and Saturn in September of 6 BC.

Astronomical tables of the Chinese record the triple conjunction event in 4 BC. They also record something strange: the appearance of an "evanescent" star between Saturn and Jupiter for a brief period in February of

4 BC. Kepler noted the same thing in 1603-1604: a new "extraordinary, brilliant star" was visible when the three planets came into conjunction. Scholars speculate this was a comet. The comet or the conjunction may have been the Star of Bethlehem. Either way, plenty of evidence suggests a sign appeared in the heavens at the time of Jesus' birth[233,234].

I looked in astrology books. The Age of Pisces began around the time of the birth of Jesus. The symbol for Pisces is the fish. That is also the Christian symbol for Jesus. The Star of Bethlehem was visible in the Constellation Pisces. The conjunction of Saturn, Jupiter, and Mars, and the "evanescent comet" which were the Star of Bethlehem, appear every 805 years—7 BC, AD 798, and AD 1603. The next Star of Bethlehem's appearance will be in AD 2408![235]

The Magi: From Jerusalem, the alignment of planets could be seen to the south, directly over Bethlehem, which is four miles away. That is how the Magi found Jesus. Bethlehem was a small town of only a few families.

In my opinion, the Magi were probably the descendants of Hebrews from Persia, perhaps from the ten lost tribes of northern Israel taken to Persia by the Assyrians. The Magi were familiar with the prophecies of the books of *Numbers* and *Daniel*. "There shall come a star out of Jacob and a scepter shall rise out of Israel." (*Numbers* 24:17)

A scepter is the symbol of a king. They knew it was time for a king to be born in Israel.

In AD 614, when the Persians conquered Jerusalem, they set about destroying the city. However, in Bethlehem, they came upon a fresco of the Magi presenting gifts to Jesus. They did not destroy the fresco because they were familiar with the story of the Magi. It was known throughout Persia, which may be proof that it occurred[236,237].

Month of birth: Old One wrote Jesus was born in October. Evidence corroborating this claim involves John the Baptist. According to the Bibilical author Luke, the father of John the Baptist, Zacharias, was a Levitical priest of the order of Abijah. When Zacharias was in the temple, he was told by an angel his wife had conceived a son. In *1 Chronicles* 24 it states the priests of the order of Abijah were assigned to the temple in the Hebrew month of Sivan. The Hebrew month of Sivan was part of June and part of July. So John the Baptist was conceived in June or July. His mother, Elizabeth, became pregnant in June or July.

According to *Luke* 1:26-55, Mary, the mother of Jesus, became pregnant during the sixth month of Elizabeth's pregnancy. Since Elizabeth conceived in June or July, her sixth month of pregnancy would be December or January. Mary conceived in December or January. So, Jesus would be born nine months later, in September or October!

Another way to corroborate the October date is with the Elijah prophecy—John the Baptist was the reincarnation of Elijah. There is a Jewish tradition that Elijah will come back at Passover. If you believe John the Baptist was the reincarnation of Elijah, then, according to Jewish tradition, he was born at Passover. The feast of Passover is always in the spring: March or April. According to Luke, Mary was three months pregnant when John the Baptist was born. Six months later, Mary gave birth to Jesus. Add six months to Passover, and you have the month of October[238,239].

The shepherds: On the road from Jerusalem to Bethlehem were the temple flocks of the Migdal Eder Watchtower. Shepherds tended the flocks year round. Luke wrote "there were shepherds abiding in the fields by night." (*Luke* 2:8) That was correct. They were tending the flocks of the Migdal Eder Watchtower for the temple in Jerusalem[240].

The massacre of the innocents: It was very difficult to find information on Herod's massacre of the infants of Bethlehem. It is only recorded in *Matthew,* not *Mark*, *Luke*, or *John*. Also, the Roman/Jewish historian Josephus does not mention the massacre in the *Antiquities of the Jews*. I believe the reason is because so few of the babies of Bethlehem were actually killed. According to the evidence I could find, most had fled with their parents before Herod's soldiers had arrived[241].

The *Protevangelium of James*, one of the Gospels not included in the Bible, mentions the massacre. It also tells about Elizabeth and her son, John the Baptist, fleeing to the wilderness. In addition, it mentions that Elizabeth's husband, Zacharias, was murdered by Herod's soldiers.

Some scholars have suggested John the Baptist spent his youth in the wilderness because *Luke* 1:80 says John was in the wilderness until his public appearance to Israel. This may have been because he fled to the wilerness with his mother, Elizabeth, to escape Herod[242].

An Israeli archaeologist, named Shimon Gibson, believes he has found a cave where John the Baptist had fled to. The cave has pottery from the period of Jesus' birth and paintings on the walls of a man in a hairy garment. It also had a stone with an imprint of a foot, used for foot anointing. The cave is in the desert near Bethlehem[243].

In the fourth century AD, a philosopher named Ambrosius Macrobius wrote the *Saturnalia*. He included a story of Herod killing children younger than two[244].

Macrobius placed the story in Syria and states one of Herod's sons was among those killed. He claims Caesar Augustus, upon hearing of the massacre, said "I'd rather be Herod's pig than Herod's son." (Herod did not eat pork.) Augustus was the Roman Caesar at the time of Jesus' birth. There was no written record of a massacre of children in Syria by Herod before this. Some scholars believe Macrobius may have been writing of Herod's Bethlehem massacre, because Israel was considered part of Syria. Syria and Israel were under the same governor[245].

It was in Herod's character to massacre children, or anyone he considered a threat[246]. So there is some evidence the massacre, or an attempted massacre, took place.

However, the number of children killed may only have been a few, if any at all. And possibly, Zacharias, the father of John the Baptist, was killed by Herod's soldiers.

The flight to Egypt: Christian churches and monuments all over Egypt claim they are on a site where Jesus' family spent time hiding from Herod. The most well-known place is the Monastery of the Holy Virgin at Al-Muharraq, Egypt[247].

In addition, some of the *Infancy Gospels* talk about the time in Egypt. They mention miracles performed by Jesus as an infant in Egypt. (The *Infancy Gospels* were not included in the New Testament.)

Accounts in both *Luke* and *Matthew* agree that eventually Jesus and his family settled in Nazareth, which was in Gallilee.

Jesus and the east: I already had a lot of information on Jesus' time in the east. Remember my trip to Afghanistan, Mena, and Becky's e-mail[248]?

Once again, I have to say Old One's version of the Truth was correct. It can be corroborated in every detail! Now I will go into Old One's main points about the life of Jesus. Again, my research and references are at the end of the outline.

1. Jesus' baptism by John the Baptist was not mentioned.

2. Jesus returned from the east, and then spent time in the desert with Enki, whom I have come to believe is the Biblical devil. Old One did not call Enki "the devil." He wrote that with Enki, Jesus determined what His message to the Hebrews would be. He also agreed to teach the Gentiles among them. He did not repeat John the Baptist's message of "repent, because the Kingdom of God is coming." Instead, He taught the Kingdom of God is here. It is within us and all around us. He taught how to

230

become a part of the Kingdom.

3. After His time in the desert with Enki, Jesus returned to Nazareth and went to the local temple service. During the service, He was asked to read a passage from the Scriptures. He read from *Isaiah*: 61:1-2, which says "The spirit of the Lord is on me, because he has anointed me to preach good news to the poor. He has sent me to proclaim freedom for the prisoners and recovery of sight for the blind, to release the oppressed, to proclaim the year of the Lord's favor."

Then Old One wrote the same thing it says in *Luke* 4:19:21: "Then He rolled up the scroll, gave it back to the attendant, and sat down. The eyes of everyone in the synagogue were fastened on Him, and He began by saying to them, 'today this scripture is fulfilled in your hearing.'"

4. This greatly upset the leaders of the synagogue. They chased Jesus out of the synagogue to the edge of a hill but stopped short of throwing Him over the hill. He left Nazareth and went to Capernaum. There He performed healings and taught about the Kingdom of God around us and in us.

5. At Capernaum, He was confronted by some family members. Jesus was in a house. They called to Him. Jesus answered "Who are my mother and brothers?" Then He looked at those seated around Him and said "Here are my mother and brothers. Whoever does God's will is my brother and sister and mother." Then He said something for which He is often misquoted: "Whoever does not set aside his father in my way will not be able to be a disciple to me. And whoever does not love his father and his mother in my way will not be a disciple to me."

This was from the Gospel of *Thomas*, saying 101. *Thomas* was not included in the New Testament.

The second part of saying 101 about "love" is often left out of this quote. Also, the Aramaic word "snh" which means "set aside" is often mistranslated as "hate." So, some people claim Jesus said to hate your father, which is a misquote[252].

6. John the Baptist was arrested. While in prison, he sent one of his disciples to Jesus. The disciple asked Jesus "Are you the One who is to come, or are we to expect some other?"

Jesus answered, "Go and tell John what you hear and see: the blind receive their sight and the lame walk, lepers are cleansed and the deaf hear, and the dead are raised up, and the poor have good news preached to them. And blessed is he who takes no offense." (*Matthew* 11:2-6)

Jesus was saying He is the Messiah. The list of achievements in Jesus' answer were from Isaiah's prophecies: *Isaiah* 61:1, *Isaiah* 26:19, and *Isaiah* 35:3-6. Jesus was saying He had fulfilled Isaiah's prophecies about what the Messiah would do.

7. According to Old One, Jesus used the dinner meal to spread His ideas. He did not follow the Hebrew meal traditions, where seating was by hierarchical rank. Equality was emphasized. Jesus' meals recognized all participants as coequals with no class distinction. Jesus used this as a model for socialization. He made no distinction of rank and status[253].

8. Old One said Jesus moved away from John the Baptist's call to the Hebrews to repent because Yahweh, the vengeful God, was returning. Instead, He emphasized God's mercy and inclusiveness. He met with Gentiles, ate with sinners, and touched the sick. He said: "It is not the healthy who need a doctor, but the sick. I have not come to call the right-eous, but sinners." (*Mark* 2:17)

9. Jesus treated women equally. Women were an oppressed segment of the Hebrew population. He violated the customs of the Hebrews in al-most all of His dealings with women: women traveled with Him and His band of followers. They sat at His dinner tables. Jesus asked the Samaritan woman for help and accepted a prostitute's anointing of oil with gratitude and defended her. Jesus taught women as disciples.

In the days of Jesus, Hebrew men said a prayer to Yahweh: "Blessed art thou, O Lord, who hast not made me a woman." Women sat in sepa-rate sections and were rarely permitted to talk to men outside of their families. They were rarely allowed to learn the Torah[254].

Jesus is quoted as saying He will make Mary (Magdalene) male so "she too may become a living spirit…For every woman who will make herself male will enter the Kingdom of Heaven." This is from *Thomas*, saying 114. Remember, *Thomas* is not in the New Testament.

Jesus is often criticized as being sexist for this statement by those who do not understand. Jesus meant that by teaching Mary Magdalene, He will make her equal to men. All women should be taught, to be able to enter the Kingdom of Heaven, just like men. He will make women "male."

10. Jesus preached the Sermon on the Mount and other Buddhist be-liefs. He taught Enki's message to humans about the Creator of All, rein-carnation, and spiritual growth. He taught that we have a soul. Jesus' fol-lowers did not fast, and discarded many of the rules of the Torah given to Moses by Enlil/Yahweh.

11. Jesus taught His closest followers information about the gods of Sumer. This was kept a secret from most of the Hebrews. By Jesus' teachings, Enlil/Yahweh was transformed into the Creator of All.

12. Jesus gave humans self-empowerment. We are no longer the fearful subjects of a vengeful, jealous god.

At this point, it is probably a good time to tell you some information about these twelve points I found while doing research at home.

The baptism of Jesus: Old One did not mention the baptism of Jesus! The story of the baptism of Jesus is mentioned in the Bible, in *Matthew, Mark, Luke* and *John*. I never thought much about this story, just assuming it was true. It marked the beginning of Jesus' ministry. During the baptism described in *Mark,* the heavens open and a voice from "heaven" says "You are my beloved Son; with you I am well pleased." (*Mark* 1:9-11) In *Matthew,* the account is the same except John says to Jesus "I need to be baptized by you, and do you come to me?" (*Matthew* 3:14) *Luke* has just about the same account. In *John*, it says John the Baptist proclaimed: "Behold the Lamb of God, who takes away the sins of the world." (*John* 1:29)

Old One does not mention the baptism, as if it didn't happen. Why did Jesus need to be baptized if He was the Messiah? Also curious was how St. Paul, in his epistles, never mentioned John the Baptist in connection with Jesus' mission.

Here is a good question: If John was preparing the way for Jesus, why did he keep preaching after he baptized Jesus? Shouldn't his job have been over? Shouldn't his followers have left him, and followed Jesus[257]?

A real telling event is John, after his imprisonment, sent a messenger to ask Jesus if He was the one who was to come, or should he look for another. (*Matthew* 11:3)

If John had baptized Jesus, and the heavens opened, proclaiming Jesus to be God's son, John would not have to ask that question.

In my opinion, Old One seemed to be correct in omitting the story of the baptism of Jesus by John the Baptist.

The temptation in the wilderness: This was one story I never believed because I didn't think the devil existed. According to the Bible, the devil met Jesus in the desert after Jesus had fasted and prayed for forty days. The devil told Jesus to turn stones into bread to prove He was the Son of God. Jesus replied "Man does not live by bread alone, but by the word of God." Then the devil took Jesus to the highest point of the temple in

Jerusalem and dared Jesus to throw Himself down and let the angels catch Him. Jesus replied "Do not put God to the test." Next, the devil took Jesus to a high mountain and showed Him "all of the kingdoms of the world." The devil said "all this I will give you if you bow down and worship me." Jesus replied, "worship the Lord your God only." This was recorded in *Matthew* 4:1-11 and *Luke* 4:1-13.

I'd have to say Old One's version of Jesus' time in the desert makes more sense to me than the Bible's version. Jesus met with Enki instead of an entity called the devil. First, going onto the roof of the Jerusalem temple or one of the towers and standing there is a highly improbable scenario. And, Jesus was supposed to be in the desert, not Jerusalem. Second, there is no high mountain where anyone can see "all of the kingdoms of the world[257]."

It is plausible the devil referred to in the Bible was Enki, and not some evil spirit-type being. Enki was regarded as the devil by the Hebrews because that is how he was portrayed in the story of the Garden of Eden. It is also possible they discussed what Jesus' message and teachings would be.

I found something that may corroborate this possibility. The followers of John the Baptist believed Jesus spread the message of the devil. There were confrontations between the early Christians and the followers of John the Baptist. The Baptist's followers became the Mandeans and resisted converting to Christianity. John the Baptist preached about the return of the vengeful God, Enlil/Yahweh. Jesus taught about spiritual growth and self-empowerment, Enki's message to his creation, humans[258]. So if I have to choose between the two versions, I guess it will be Old One's version.

Equality: Old One's explanation of what Jesus did with the dinner meal and His ideas of equality and inclusiveness agree with the Bible. These same ideas brought trouble for Jesus in India. The Brahmin priests who presided over the Hindu caste system wanted to kill him[259]!

So at least there is consistency in these stories.

Buddhist ideas: I had learned from Mena in Afghanistan that Jesus had studied Buddhism. It seemed to me the Sermon on the Mount (my favorite teaching of Jesus!) was teaching about Karma, a Buddhist belief[250]. Old One said Jesus taught Buddhist ideas in Israel.

Here are some Buddhist teachings I have found not mentioned by Old One:

1. Jesus called for praying alone in silence. This resembles meditation, a Buddhist practice.

2. Jesus ended animal sacrificing, which was a common practice for the Hebrews. The Buddhists ended animal sacrificing, a common practice among Hindus.

3. Jesus preached nonviolence; turning the other cheek. Buddhism preaches nonviolence also.

4. The Sermon on the Mount resembles verses from a Buddhist text called the Dhammapada.

5. Jesus said "Do unto others as you would have them do unto you." Buddha said "Consider others as yourself."

6. Jesus' claim that the Kingdom of God is within us resembles the Hindu teaching that there is a master God-spirit in everything, including the God within each of us—our soul. This is from the Hindu Upanishad texts.

7. There are strange similarities between some Catholic practices and Buddhist practices: ringing bells in services, rosary beads, celibacy among Buddhist monks and Catholic priests, and many others[251,260]!

Old One seems to be correct about the connection between Christianity and Buddhism.

Inside information: Old One wrote Jesus taught only His closest followers about the gods of Sumer. There is some confirmation of this in the Gospels:

Jesus taught in parables, and according to *Mark* 4:34: "[B]ut without a parable spake He not unto His disciples, and when they were alone, He expounded all things to His disciples."

Nazareth: Old One wrote that the leaders of the synagogue in Nazareth chased Jesus to the edge of a hill. The small town of Nazareth is situated so that one part ends on a small cliff[255]!

The Second Coming:
For Those of Us Who Are Perplexed,
This Is the Explanation

Old One quoted *Matthew* 24 and called it Jesus' information about His Second Coming. It began with a scene of Jesus in the temple in Jerusalem. Many wealthy men were making large donations for the upkeep of the temple. A poor woman came forward and gave a small donation—two lepta. Some men in the temple ridiculed the amount she gave. Jesus responded that what the woman gave was a greater donation than anyone else because she gave all she had[261].

I picked my head up and thought about this. Jesus made a really beautiful observation. It was the *true* Christianity. Just then, a grainy, irritating voice penetrated my brain.

"That must be a really interesting book." The guy with the ponytail and bald head was speaking to me!

"Oh, yeah, I, um, it's, ah, it's a good book," I barely got out.

"You haven't looked up once. What's it called?"

I was getting annoyed. I didn't feel like talking. I wanted to read about the Second Coming. Then I thought, *Jesus would not be rude.*

"It doesn't really have a name. I guess it could be called The Truth."

He looked at me quizzically for a moment. "Then it couldn't have anything to do with George Bush." So, he was trying to pick an argument. That was even more annoying.

"Actually, I think he has something to do with this."

I was thinking about the NASA missions to Mars. And, I wouldn't have been in Iraq if George Bush had not been elected President. According to Al Gore, Bush's opponent in the 2000 election, he would not have invaded Iraq if he had been elected President.

"That's impossible!" He laughed as he kept looking at me, waiting for a response.

I thought about telling him I was just coming back from Iraq, and that I did a lot of good things there, but then decided against it. His mind was made up. He believed what he wanted to be true. I made a little fake laugh and began reading again.

The disciples commented to Jesus about the magnificent stones of the temple walls. Jesus said "No stone will be left standing on another; every one will be thrown down." (*Matthew* 24:2)

Later, as Jesus was sitting on the Mount of Olives, the disciples came to Him privately. They said "tell us, when will this happen, and what will be the sign of your coming and of the end of the age?" (*Matthew* 24:3)

Jesus did not answer the question of when the temple walls would collapse. However, He told them about the signs of His coming and the signs of the end of the age.

According to Old One, the important signs are these:

1. The sign of the Son of Man will appear in the sky. (*Matthew* 24:30)

2. No one knows the day or the hour, only the father in heaven. Just as in the days before the flood, people knew nothing about what would happen until the flood came. That is how it will be at the Second Coming of Man. (*Matthew* 24:38-39)

3. The Gospel of the Kingdom will be preached to all nations. (*Matthew* 24:14)

4. The twigs of the fig tree will get tender and its leaves will come out. (*Matthew* 24:12)

5. Famines and earthquakes will occur in many places. (*Matthew* 24:7)

6. Because of the increase of wickedness, the love of most will grow cold. (*Matthew* 24:12)

7. The Sun will be darkened and the moon will not give its light. (*Matthew* 24:29)[262]

If you do not believe Jesus' prophecies about His return, consider this. Jesus said the temple walls would fall and "no stone would be left upon another stone." This came true around AD 70, about thirty-eight years after His death and resurrection.

In AD 68, the Jews rebelled against the Romans. In response, the Romans surrounded the city of Jerusalem and laid siege to it. No one could get in or out of the city for two years. There was much suffering in Jerusalem, but the Jewish rebels would not surrender to the Romans, luring them into traps and killing Roman soldiers. When the Romans finally broke through the Jewish defenses, in AD 70, they destroyed Jerusalem. The soldiers were so angry about the prolonged siege they even burned down the temple. Large amounts of gold and silver that had been stored in the temple melted during the fire. To get the melted gold and silver, the Roman soldiers pried apart the stones of the temple walls with crowbars. As a result, no stone was left upon another stone, just as Jesus had predicted[263]!

Old One explained Jesus' predictions about the Second Coming. However, he said we have to add predictions from the Book of Revelations.

"And I saw thrones, and they sat upon them and judgment was given unto them…And they lived and reigned with Christ a thousand years." (*Revelation* 20:4) According to Old One, this means when Jesus comes back to Earth, He will reign for one thousand years—not longer—for a specific reason. If you keep reading the *Book of Revelation*, it says at the end of the one thousand years, the devil will be let loose again.

I Peter 3:7,10 explains what will happen after the devil is loosened: the Earth will be destroyed by fire and the heavens will disappear with a roar! The story continues in *Revelation* 21:1-4. After the first heaven and Earth pass away, the Holy City, the New Jerusalem, will come out of heaven from God. "Now the dwelling of God is with men, and He will live with them."

These prophecies explain our future!

I will provide you with an explanation of Old One's prophecies as his writing explained them to me.

1. *The sign of the Son of Man will appear in the sky.* The sign of the Son of Man is the Star of Bethlehem. It appears every 805 years. So Jesus gave us a very good clue about when He will return. The last time the Star of Bethlehem appeared was in AD 1603, recorded by Johannes Kepler. The next Star of Bethlehem will appear in AD 2408. We have to add to this clue what is says in the books of *Revelation* and *I Peter.*

Revelation and *I Peter* tell us Jesus will reign for one thousand years, and then the Earth will be destroyed by fire and the heavens will disappear. By "heavens," ancient texts are usually referring to the home of the gods, Planet X, the brown dwarf star. (Remember Ricky's explanation of heaven?)

The most likely reason for the Earth to be destroyed by fire, and Planet X disappearing, is the gravitational effect of the Sun and the brown dwarf star as they pass near to each other. This will cause volcanoes, earthquakes, and collisions with comets.

The brown dwarf star passes the Sun about every 3,600 years[266]. The next passing of the brown dwarf star will be around AD 3400 because the last passing was just before the birth of Jesus. Remember the research about Planet X! If you put Jesus' clue together with the *Revelation* texts and *I Peter*, it means Jesus' Second Coming will be around AD 2408. He will reign for one thousand years until around AD 3400. Then the Earth will be destroyed by fire from comets, earthquakes, and volcanoes as the brown dwarf star passes. The planet of the gods that revolves around the brown dwarf star will be completely destroyed. Then the leader of the gods of Planet X will establish a New Jerusalem on Earth. The dwelling of the gods will be with men.

Revelation describes the New Jerusalem as being 1,500 miles long and 1,500 miles high, and in the shape of a pyramid. I'm not sure what that means, but that is what it says.

Jesus gave another clue about His Second Coming. He said these things would occur before this generation passes. By one generation, Jesus may have meant one complete revolution by the brown dwarf star around the sun. So, all of His predictions will happen by AD 3400, when the brown dwarf star, Planet X, returns. The Elohim who were alive in Jesus' time will still be alive in AD 3400, and will see everything.

I remembered reading the prophecies of Nostradamus when I was in college. Nostradamus was a physician from the Middle Ages, whom many believe has been able to predict the future. He predicted the world would come to an end in AD 3797 because the sun will expand. In my opinion, Nostradamus was predicting the same thing as Jesus. As the brown dwarf star gets closer, there will be more solar flares and sun spots. Maybe that is what he meant by the sun expanding. I believe his dating was off by four hundred years, but…! [267,268]

2. *No one knows the day or the hour, except the Father in Heaven.* Those in Heaven are the Elohim, and the Elohim know approximately when this will happen. They are preparing for it. They are preparing us, humanity, for it.

3. *The Gospel of the Kingdom* has already been preached to all nations. Christian missionaries continue teaching the Gospels to all nations.

4. *The fig tree sprouts leaves.* Many Bible experts believe this refers to Israel and the expansion of its territory. Israel was created in 1948 and has expanded its borders in subsequent wars[264].

5. *Famines and earthquakes will occur in many places.* There have always been famines and earthquakes. Here are some of the famines that have taken place over the last few decades, and they are massive in scale[269]:

Location	Year	Number Dead
Ukraine	1932-1933	5 million
China	1941	2.5 million
USSR	1946	Unknown
India	1965-1967	1.5 million
Ethiopia	1974	250,000
Niger	1974	100,000
Mozambique	1980s	Unknown
Cambodia	1975-1980	3 million
Ethiopia	1984-1985	1 million
Sudan	1991-1998	800,000
North Korea	2002-2005	Undetermined
Horn of Africa	2004-2005	Undetermined

Earthquakes have been increasing in frequency for the last few decades. According to the U.S. Geological Survey Earthquake Report, from 1900-1949 we averaged three major earthquakes per decade, nine in the 1950s, thirteen in the 1960s, fifty-six in the 1970s, seventy-four in the 1980s, and 120 in the 1990s. So earthquakes are occurring in many places.

6. *Because of the increase of wickedness, the love of most will grow cold.* In my opinion, that has happened, and continues to get worse. Just look around. I wonder how terrorists can kill innocent people in barbaric ways and be proud of it.

7. The last item was *the sun will be darkened and the moon will not shine.* Old One did not explain this one. Projected solar eclipses all the way through AD 2460 show only two or three per year. Maybe this means Jesus will come to Earth during a solar eclipse. In 2408, the eclipses are scheduled for February 27 and August 22. [270]

End of the age: According to Old One, the "age" the disciples referred to was a Zodiac Age. This was a surprise to me. I never paid a serious thought to the signs of the zodiac. Evidently, one cycle in the sky of all twelve of the zodiac signs spans 25,626.83 years. That is equal to the "Great Year" of the Mayan calendar. You're probably wondering what this has to do with the Second Coming of Jesus. Well, here's the explanation.

The Mayan Great Year ends in the year AD 2012. The Mayan calendar also ends in the year AD 2012. The Age of Pisces (whose symbol is the fish, also the symbol of Christianity and Jesus) began in AD 26 and will end in AD 2012, lasting for 1,986 years.

Here are the different ages and their durations:

Aries, Pisces, Libra, Virgo	1,986.37 years each
Aquarius, Scorpio, Leo, Taurus	2,129.04 years each
Capricorn, Sagittarius, Cancer, Gemini	2,291.28 years each

The next age will be Aquarius. There are two interesting characteristics of Aquarius. The first is that it is associated with a time of peace. The return of Jesus will start the one thousand years of peace in the Age of Aquarius! The second characteristic of Aquarius is, astrologically, the planet Uranus rules this age. According to Sumerian texts, Uranus is associated with Anu, the supreme ruler of the gods of Planet X. So after the next passing of the brown dwarf star, Anu will rule the Earth. That will be in AD 3400, when the New Jerusalem is established. That is our destiny! (265, 271)

Maybe the Mayans knew what was going to happen. They knew the Age of Pisces was going to be the last age of mankind. That is why their calendar ended. Old One and the gods of Sumer know what will happen as the brown dwarf star approaches: the Second Coming of Jesus, one thousand years of peace, and the New Jerusalem.

The "End Times" are four hundred years away!

Death of the Messiah

The "fasten your seat belt" sign began flashing, and the pilot said we were approaching Reagan National Airport for a landing. I was disappointed. I wanted to finish Old One's manuscript. I put it into my carry-on bag and fastened my seat belt, trying to ignore Strange Man staring at me out of the corner of his eye. He was beginning to give me the creeps. I couldn't wait to get off of the plane and away from him.

Strange Man tried to start a conversation. "That must really have been a good book."

"Uh, yes, it was." I looked away, out the window, pretending I was very interested in watching the landing. That didn't work.

"Do you fly very much?"

"What? Oh, no, I don't."

"I don't either," he said.

"Oh." I was trying to say as little as possible.

Strange Man kept looking right at me, and I kept looking away.

"So, do you live in D.C.?" he asked.

"Sometimes."

"Sometimes? How do you live in D.C. sometimes?"

He was full of questions.

"I live different places for work," I answered.

"Oh, me too," he said. "I go to Europe a lot. I love to go to Europe. Especially France." I thought he said he didn't fly a lot!

I didn't respond, so he kept on talking. "The Europeans are great. They're so much more, what's the right word, like, enlightened or something, than we are."

"Yeah." I was keeping to my plan—short answers.

This guy was a real pain. I felt like arguing with him about that last statement, but I didn't. I just wanted him to stop talking. The Europeans, the people who gave us the Kaiser, Hitler, Stalin, Colonialism, Nazis, Facism, Communism, the Berlin Wall, and the Iron Curtain, are more enlightened. I read an article on the Internet about a French island where they use live dogs for shark bait! How enlightened[272].

Strange Man kept saying things about Europe, and I continued responding "yeah." Finally, the plane landed. I hurried away from Strange Man as soon as I had the chance.

When I got to my townhouse, I didn't even unpack, calling my sister June in Pittsburgh, and making arrangements to drive to her house and meet at 8:00 AM. Then we would drive another ninety minutes to Ohio and Aunt Sophia's funeral. I should have gone right to sleep, but I was almost at the end of Old One's manuscript. I had to finish reading. Picking up the manuscript, I sat down on my couch. I didn't want to lie in bed because I would probably fall asleep. I continued with the manuscript.

The writing continued with the sacrifice of Jesus' life and how it made more sense two thousand years ago than it does now, especially to the gods of Sumer. First, consider that human sacrifice was practiced in many ancient cultures. The victims were killed in a manner meant to please or appease the gods[273].

1. Ancient Greeks sacrificed maidens to the god Artemis.

2. During the Celtic revolt against the Romans, it is reported the leader, Boudicca, impaled Roman prisoners as offerings to gods.

3. The Gauls built wicker cages, put living humans in them, and then burned them as a sacrifice to the gods.

4. The ancient Chinese sacrificed young men and women to the river gods. They also buried slaves alive as part of a funeral service.

5. The Aztecs made ritual sacrifice to many gods. For the god Xipec-Totec, the victim had to be bound to a post and shot full of arrows. The dead victim would then be skinned. The god Tlaloc required the death of weeping male children. It was written in Aztec texts that they sacrificed eighty-four thousand prisoners for the dedication of the great temple at Tenochtitlan!

6. The Carthaginians and some Canaanite tribes sacrificed their children to the gods.

7. The ancient Hindus of India practiced human sacrifice. As recently as 2003, adherents of an Indian religion called Tantrism sacrificed twenty-five humans in the Utter Pradesh province of India[274].

So it appears human sacrifice was common and accepted in the ancient world. That brings us to the gods of Sumer. If you remember Old One's creation story, Enki created us by mixing the DNA of an Elohim with the DNA of a hominid. There is a Sumerian text that describes this, and also tells of the killing of an Elohim to provide a soul for the new creation. This was done three times per month. The Elohim was told of his "token" before he was sacrificed. The text leads one to believe the Elohim allowed himself to be sacrificed willingly, and it was done in a ritual manner. The gods of Sumer had no reservations about sacrificing living gods, and indeed required the sacrifice of living humans[275].

That brings us to a famous Biblical sacrifice, Abraham and Isaac. Most depictions of this story in the Bible and paintings portray Isaac as being around twelve to fourteen years old. However, Old One wrote Isaac was an adult and willingly allowed Abraham to bind his arms and prepare him for sacrifice. I was not able to verify this. However, it seems human sacrifice was accepted, even desired, to please the gods. The ancient belief in quick reincarnation, as the result of a violent death, made the victim more willing to be sacrificed. They believed they would live again.

Another example of human sacrifice, according to Old One, was the Hebrew conquest of Canaan. All prisoners of the Hebrews were slaughtered to please Yahweh.

I never thought of that as human sacrifice but I guess it was.

In the ancient world, human sacrifice, including that of children, was common. This leads to the conclusion that Jesus, the Son of Man, as He called Himself, was sacrificed to please the gods; to make peace between humans and the gods. Today, it is difficult to comprehend how this makes peace, but it was a common practice of the Elohim and ancient peoples.

I thought about that. Old One was right. Human sacrifice doesn't make sense to a modern person. However, it was perfectly clear to the ancient peoples. The Greeks sacrificed maidens to the gods. Carthaginians sacrificed their children to the gods. Abraham was going to sacrifice Isaac, his son, to Yahweh. The Son of Man was sacrificed to Enlil/Yahweh and the gods of Sumer.

Old One wrote that on the night of Jesus' arrest, he prayed to the gods, asking for the sacrifice to be called off. Remember what Old One had said about the Elohim? They could communicate without speaking, and over great distances!

The sacrifice was not called off and Jesus fulfilled the prophecies. After the sacrifice, Jesus was resurrected by two Elohim who were still in the tomb when Mary Magdalene arrived on Sunday morning. The resurrection could be a sign the sacrifice had been accepted by the gods.

Jesus was then taken to heaven, Planet X, by the Elohim. This was the Ascension. So Jesus made peace with the gods of Sumer, fulfilled the prophecies of the Messiah, and taught us about the Kingdom within us and around us, reincarnation and karma, and equality. He will return in the same way He left to set up the kingdom of the gods. Then the gods will come down to Earth and create the New Jerusalem after their planet is destroyed with the next passing of the brown dwarf star.

If my old Sunday school teacher was reading this, she would think I had completely lost it. I think she died a few years ago, so she won't read this. Thank goodness, or God, or the Elohim.

To me, Old One's interpretation of the Bible, the gods of Sumer, and Jesus makes more sense than the Sunday school version of the Bible. And it can be corroborated by scientific, archaeological evidence, or other ancient texts. That is what has been demonstrated in this book[276].

The Sequel

Old One wrote it was important to know about some things that happened after Jesus left the earth. He began with the story of St. Paul of Tarsus.

In the Old Testament accounts, St. Paul, a Hebrew Pharisee, had persecuted the early Christians in an effort to stop the Christian movement. Paul's name was originally Saul, and he changed it to Paul after converting to Christianity. One day, while traveling with companions, he was blinded by a bright light and knocked to the ground. A voice came out of the light. It said: "Saul, Saul, why do you persecute me? It is hard to kick against the goad." (Acts 9:4)

Paul believed Jesus had blinded him, and from that day, he preached that Jesus was the Messiah. He believed it was his duty to preach to the non-Jews, the Gentiles. However, Paul was a Pharisee, and taught in the context of what the Pharisees believed; resurrection instead of reincarnation. He taught when Jesus comes back, all the dead will resurrect and be judged by the Messiah. Paul also adhered to the Old Testament laws and rituals, and taught this to the Romans and other Gentiles[277].

According to Old One, it was not Jesus who blinded Paul. It was a messenger of Enlil/Yahweh. The messengers (angels) of the Elohim had blinded others. It appears to have been one of their ways to subdue humans. Remember the two Elohim messengers who blinded the townspeople of Sodom. Also, the Elohim who resurrected Jesus blinded the Roman guards at the tomb. So, it makes sense that a messenger of Enlil/Yahweh blinded Paul, not Jesus.

Paul's companions did not come to his aid. Instead, they watched and then carried out the Elohim's command to take Paul to a particular house in a nearby town. Paul's companions were afraid of the Elohim[277].

Paul was also subdued with their prods. That's what the Elohim messenger meant when he said, "It is hard to kick against the goads." Goads are like cattle prods. They used them to keep Paul on the ground until he was pacified. In my opinion, Jesus would not have done this. It was an Elohim messenger.

The real proof is that Jesus had ascended into heaven long before the blinding of Paul. So Jesus did not cause Paul's blindness.

Paul's blindness lasted for three days, and then he went out among the Gentiles, preaching Jesus was the Messiah who will return. He preached that when Jesus returns, everyone who ever lived will resurrect and be judged by Jesus[278].

This belief was the one some Elohim wanted to spread among the humans. We must submit to Enlil/Yahweh's will because Jesus is coming back to judge us. Old One wrote this is a way for the Elohim to maintain control over us, in preparation for the New Jerusalem. This was in contrast to Jesus' and Enki's teachings of free will and reincarnation. According to Old One, this was the reason for the incident with Paul, and for the Council at Constantinople, which tried to suppress the teaching of reincarnation. The next important event concerned the god Nannar.

Nannar was also known as Sin, the moon god. Unsatisfied with the course of humanity after Jesus left, he created a new religion in which we are to completely submit to his will, the will of the gods of Sumer. He became Allah, and the Elohim messenger, Gabriel, dictated a new holy book to the prophet Mohammed. This new religion professed the Second Coming of Jesus, in which everyone that ever lived will resurrect and be judged by Jesus. It did not acknowledge reincarnation and limited free will. If you submit to Allah's will, he may give you good fortune. But then again, Allah may not give you good fortune. It is up to Allah. Allah is all powerful. Allah will destroy anyone who does not submit to his will[279].

Allah was also antagonistic towards other religions. The new God required a one-world religion. Again, according to Old One, this was to increase Elohim control over humans, to prepare for the New Jerusalem[280]. However, a great surprise happened to the Elohim—America.

America did away with kingship, which had been instituted by the Elohim. (Remember the Sumerian King's List.) America encouraged freedom; rule of the people, by the people, and for the people, free will, and individualism. Americans probably would not be submissive participants to a world takeover by the Elohim at the Second Coming.

As a result, the Elohim have been trying to destroy or change America since it was founded. Nazism, Japanese imperialism, and Communism were all attempts by the Elohim to end the American idea of individual freedom and of rule by the people. (And I had blamed it on the Europeans!) Old One wrote that radical Islam and the globalization movements are other attempts to end the idea of individual freedom and rule by the people.

These "American ideals" are the teachings of Enki: individual freedom and rule by the people. Enki was portrayed as the devil, Satan, in the Torah and in the Bible. According to Old One, that is why some Moslem leaders who have studied the scriptures call America the Great Satan. America is a follower of Enki. On the American dollar is a pyramid and the "All Seeing Eye," symbols from Enki's territory, Egypt[280].

Old One claims the Americans have been as clever as the Elohim in their quest to turn humanity against the gods of Sumer. On their dollar bills are the Latin words "Annuit Coeptis." This means "God has favored our undertakings." The Americans claim God is on their side. They proclaim this to the world, while spreading individual freedom, the message of Enki, the devil.

Another motto of the Americans is "Novus Ordo Seclorum," "New World Order[281]." I remembered George Bush, Sr. using that motto many times during the Gulf War. The New World Order is the end of the Elohim kingships of gods and demigods and the beginning of the self-rule of humanity. I thought about Japanese imperialism, and when the Japanese surrendered to the Americans after the dropping of the atom bombs. One of the conditions of the surrender was that the Japanese emperor, Hirohito, had to renounce his divine status to the world. He had to say he was not a descendant of the gods.

The New World Order!

I never thought about America being an enemy of the gods of Sumer, or at least those gods who opposed Enki. We are the enemy of those who want all humans to submit to the rule of the gods of Sumer.

That is why I was in Iraq.

Old One wrote that I should accept the New Jerusalem. I should not fight against it like the Americans. It is our destiny. We cannot change it, and should enjoy the benefits it will bring. When the ruler of the gods brings the New Jerusalem to Earth, he will give humans who have accepted him "everlasting life," like the Elohim. We will live for thousands of years, like Enlil, Enki, Inanna, and the others.

We will finally eat from the Tree of Life!

Joy DiNardo, now you know the Truth. Use it wisely.
Enkeln, a descendant of Marduk, God of Babylon.

The Funeral

I looked at my clock—2:00 AM! I had finished the manuscript.

I knew I shouldn't go to sleep. If I fell asleep, I wouldn't wake up. I should drink some coffee, strong coffee. Did I have any? Thank goodness. There was an old jar of instant coffee in the cabinet. I was going to have to drive all night without sleeping. But it was worth it to finish the manuscript. Or was it? Did I really want to know the Truth? Jesus was part human, part god of Sumer. The gods of Sumer created us. They will be coming back. So many thoughts were revolving in my head: Planet X, the Nephilim, gold, Noah's Flood, the Hebrew crossing of the Gulf of Aqaba, the Egyptian *Book of the Dead*, the Pyramid at Giza, the captivity in Babylon, the Star of Bethlehem, the Age of Pisces, reincarnation, resurrection, one thousand years of peace, the New Jerusalem. The Truth!

I drank two cups of instant coffee with four packs of Stevia in each. I took a quick shower, packed an overnight bag, and left for Pittsburgh. The time was 3:15 AM. It was raining in Washington, D.C. and continued all the way through Maryland. The rain stopped for a few miles around Breezewood, Pennsylvania. I took the ticket at the tollbooth for the Pennsylvania Turnpike, and the rain started again. It was pouring as I drove through the Allegheny Mountains. The sun was coming up behind me in the east. That was weird. I was driving into darkness, to the west. Finally the sun overtook me, and there was light, morning. I thought about the sun. There is global warming on Earth and Mars, not because people are driving SUVs on Earth and Mars but because the brown dwarf star is headed back toward the sun. The brown dwarf star will make a devastating passing that will destroy the heavens with a roar and the Earth with fire. Then the ruler of the gods of Sumer will bring the New Jerusalem from heaven.

The rain continued. I made it to my sister's house at 7:55 AM, very good timing. June and her husband, John, ran to the door and hugged me. I haven't talked to John for a long time. It's funny, but for a second I couldn't think of his name. Kim and I always call him June's husband. I wanted to say "Hi, June's husband." June said their son was staying at a friend's house.

Then I heard the toilet flush. June said, "Oh, grandma's here. She's coming with us." Grandma is Aunt Sophia's sister. She is eighty-seven. I guess I didn't mention Aunt Sophia was my great aunt.

Grandma came down the steps, one at a time.

"Joy, is that you?"

"Yes, it's me, grandma."

"Come here, give me a big hug. I was so worried about you in India."

"I was in Iraq, grandma."

She squeezed me. Grandma is a big woman. I couldn't breathe.

"Is it still raining?"

"Yes grandma, it's pouring."

Grandma always dressed like she was in Russia. Even though it was almost eighty degrees and steamy, she had a long dress on, with long sleeves, and a scarf over her head. It wasn't a rain scarf. It was something called a babushka. Only grandma and other ladies her age wore those things.

John got umbrellas for everyone. We walked out to John's car together under a canopy of umbrellas.

We drove back to the Pennsylvania Turnpike. The road was covered with water, and rain cascaded down the window. John turned the windshield wipers on high.

"Maybe we should have taken the ark instead of the car," John said jokingly. He doesn't usually make jokes.

"Yeah, John, go back and get the ark. Do you have all the animals ready to go?" Grandma said.

"What animals?" John didn't get grandma's joke.

"You know, the animals in Noah's Ark," Grandma explained.

John laughed. He usually doesn't laugh either. A light bulb went off in my head.

"Grandma, do you really believe that story?"

"What story?" Grandma leaned her good ear toward me.

"You know, the story of Noah's Ark," I said.

"Well, yeah, it's in the Bible." Grandma said with emphasis. If it was in the Bible, that was good enough for grandma.

"Well, it always bothered me." I was trying to be cautious. June was already frowning at me.

"What do you mean it bothered you?" Grandma was getting mad.

"It just doesn't seem very, um, plausible." I was trying to be pleasant.

Grandma was shocked. "What do you mean? It's in the Bible. It's the word of God."

"Yes, but do you really think Noah got two of every animal and put them in the ark?" I was still being pleasant.

"Well, that's what it says in the Bible. How else do you think they survived the flood?" Grandma's voice was getting louder.

"But Noah lived in the Middle East. How did he get buffaloes from North America into the ark?" It was getting harder to have a pleasant tone.

"Maybe there were some buffaloes in the Middle East." Grandma shot back an answer right away.

Buffaloes in the Middle East!

"OK, well, what about kangaroos from Australia or penguins from the Antarctic?" I forgot about being pleasant.

Grandma had an answer. "Well, maybe there were some of those in the Middle East. Didn't they have zoos?"

June was laughing. "Yeah, Noah probably got them from zoos."

Why was she butting in?

"Shut up June! What about bugs? There are thousands of different kinds of bugs, and birds!"

Grandma thought for a second. "Maybe they flew onto the ark."

OK. Great! There were buffaloes in the Middle East and Noah got kangaroos and penguins from zoos. Then all of the bugs and birds flew onto the ark.

"How about panda bears from China? Grandma, don't you think it was really impossible?"

June spoke again. "Joy, Noah put all of the animals on the ark except the unicorn."

I looked at June. "What?"

June kept going. "The unicorns wouldn't get on the ark when Noah called them. They kept running and playing in the fields. So Noah had to close the ark without them. That's why there are no unicorns today." She had a big grin on her face.

"Yeah, that's what happened to the poor unicorns." Grandma agreed. She believed that.

John, Mr. Funny, said sternly, "You just have to have faith."

I gave up!

Grandma looked out of the window. She was mad at me.

She mumbled, "I don't know why people have to question the word of God. They should believe what they were taught to believe."

We arrived at the church a little bit late. The mass was already in progress. The Orthodox priests had long beards, looking like the ancient Hebrews. The choir began to sing and I picked up a hymnbook. Aunt Sophia's casket was in the aisle. I thought about when she gave her Bible to me. I was only ten years old. The Bible had a different meaning then. It was mysterious, the word of God. Now I know so much more. I know who the gods of the Bible are: where they came from, where they are now, when they will be coming back—The Truth.

I looked down at the hymnbook. They were singing a song about the return of Jesus, when mankind will stop its warring ways and lay down its weapons. The song was called "The Peace of Our Lord." It was about the one thousand years of peace. My mind drifted off, thinking about Old One's manuscript. I was lost in my thoughts until I heard the words of the Lord's Prayer:

> "Thy Kingdom come,"
> "Thy will be done,"
> "On Earth as it is in Heaven."

People were praying for the coming of the kingdom of the gods of Sumer. Only they didn't know it.

The mass ended. The recessional hymn was about "The New Jerusalem." People were singing in joyous anticipation of the destruction of the world by fire, and the bringing of the New Jerusalem from heaven by the ruler of the gods of Sumer.

We drove to the cemetery. I was very quiet, feeling sad for Aunt Sophia. I thought about reincarnation. Maybe Aunt Sophia will live again. I actually had a strange feeling of being liberated. I'm not a sinful person who needs to be saved from the fires of hell. I was not born with original

254

sin because Adam ate an apple. I'm a good person. I need to discover the real god of the universe, not the vengeful gods of the world's religions.

It had stopped raining. The priest stood over the casket, which was sitting on a platform above the grave, and prayed. Then he took a large wooden cross and tapped it on the side of the casket, saying:

"This casket is sealed until the Second Coming of Christ."

THE END
AND
THE BEGINNING

Epilogue

The day after Aunt Sophia's funeral, June and I went to the new mall near Pittsburgh, the "Mills Mall."

I have an older car. It doesn't beep if you leave the lights on when you park. We had driven through a tunnel, and I had put my lights on. I forgot to turn them off when we parked. We shopped for over four hours. Then we tried to leave. The car made that horrible grinding sound, or is it more like a whirring sound? It did that a few times, made a clicking noise, and then it died.

I looked at June. June looked at me. She had that perturbed look, like my mother would look at me during high school when I did something stupid.

"Do you have jumper cables?"

"Um, I don't know. I'll look in the trunk."

Of course I don't have jumper cables in the trunk. June had popped the front hood. We both stood there and looked at the engine and the battery.

"I don't think I'll be able to get ahold of John right now," June said.

We both noticed a woman coming toward us that seemed to be in her early twenties.

She called out, "Hi, do you need some help?"

"Well, it's a dead battery," June said with a disgusted tone.

"Do you have jumper cables? I'll bring my car over and we can jump it."

June looked at me with an evil, piercing look.

"She doesn't have any."

"We can go into the mall," the woman suggested. "They sell them in there."

Why didn't I think of that?

"Oh, that's a good idea," I mumbled.

"C'mon. I'll go with you," the woman said enthusiastically.

"Thanks." I mumbled my answer again. June stayed by the car.

The jumper cables in the mall were twenty-seven dollars. I thought that was really expensive for jumper cables. She asked me if I had enough money. She could spare some if I didn't. I had enough. I couldn't believe she was going to give me some money.

She pulled her car next to mine and we jumped the battery. I still couldn't believe this woman was so helpful. Maybe I should offer to pay her for her trouble. I was really grateful.

"Listen, I really appreciate what you did here. Don't get mad, but I'd like to pay you something for helping us."

I grabbed my wallet and began to open it.

She put her hand up. "Oh, no, please. I'm a Christian. Good luck with your car. Don't shut the engine off for awhile. Let it run."

She got into her car and left. She was a Christian.

I am a Christian too. I follow the teachings of Yeshua, Jesus, as I now know them.

We should treat others as ourselves. Men and women are equal.

The poor in spirit will inherit the kingdom of heaven, because there is Karma.

Jesus said the kingdom of heaven is in us and around us. We are already a part of the kingdom, the spiritual kingdom. It's not the kingdom that the gods of the world's religions will be bringing.

The Creator is not the vengeful god we have been taught about.

We are not born as sinners.

The most important thing for us is our spiritual growth.

We must learn these things before THEY return.

Joy DiNardo

References

1. Blank, Wayne. 2005. "Zedekiah." <u>Daily Bible Study</u>. The Church of God. [http://www.keyway.ca/tm2001/2001225.htm].

2. de Selincourt, Aubrey. 1996. <u>Herodutus, the Histories.</u> Trans. John Marincola. New York: Penguin, pg 79-80.

3. Shearer, S.R. 2008. "The Ancient City." <u>Antipas Ministries, the End Times Network</u>. [http://www.antipasministries.com/html/file00000030.htm].

4. Pike, John. 2005. "Camp Babylon." <u>GlobalSecurity.Org</u>. [http:www.globalsecurity.org/military/ world/iraq/babylon.htm].

5. O'Connell, Daniel. 2006. "A Photo Tour, Ancient Architecture of Babylon." <u>ArchitectureAbout.Com.</u> [http://architectureabout.com/library/bl-babylon.htm].

6. Russell, Rusty. 2006. "Ancient Babylon-Nebuchadnezzar's Babylon." <u>Bible History On Line</u>. [http://biblehistory.com/ babylonia/BabyloniaNebuchadnezzarsBabylon.htm].

7. Elliott, David Vaughn. 2000. "Babylon Not Rebuilt as a City." <u>Insight into Bible Prophecy.</u> # 113. [http://insight2bp.homestead.com/files/113.html].

8. Don McAlvany's ICA. 2004. "Important Dates in the History of Gold." <u>International Collectors Associates</u>.
[http://www.mcalvany.com/ImportantDatesinGoldHistory.asp].

9. "What is Gold?" <u>Newmont, the Gold Company</u>. 2006. Newmont Mining Corporation.
[http://www.newmont.com/en/gold/goldfacts/whatis/index.asp].

10. Sitchin, Zecharia. 1990. <u>Genesis Revisited</u>. New York: Avon, pg 22.

11. "II Genesis." <u>Translation Navigating the Bible</u>. 2006. Navigating the Bible II. [http://bible.ort.org/books/pentd2.asp].

12. "II Genesis." <u>Hebrew Bible in English</u>. 2006. Navigating the Bible.
[http://bible.ort.org/books/pentd2.asp].

13. Foley, Jim. 2004. "Hominid Species." <u>Fossil Hominids FAQ</u>.
[http://www.talkorigins.org/faqs/homs/species.html].

14. See note 10 above, pg 199.

15. See note 12 above.

16. "The Watchers." <u>Fushion Anomaly</u>. 2004.
[http://fusionanomaly.net/nephilim.html].

17. Whiston, William, trans. "Antiquities of the Jews, Book II, From Creation to the Death of Isaac." <u>The Works of Flavius Josephus</u>. Christian Classics Ethereal Library.
[http://www.ccel.org/j/josephus/JOSEPHUS.HTM].

18. "Are There Lost Books of the Bible?" <u>Apologetics Press</u>.
2003. [http://www.apologeticspress.org/articles/42].

19. Heron, Patrick. 2005. <u>The Nephilim and the Pyramid of the Apocalypse.</u> Longwood, FL: Xulon Press. 24, 28.

20. Quayle, Steve. 2006. "Middle East Giants." <u>Welcome to the World of Steve Quayle</u>.
    [http://www.stevequayle.com/index1.html].

21. "Afghan Taliban Leader Orders Destruction of Ancient Statues." <u>Revolutionary Association of the Women of Afghanistan (RAWA)</u>. 2001. [http://www.rawa.org/statues.htm].

22. Prophet, Elizabeth Clare. 1987. <u>The Lost Years of Jesus</u>. Corwin Springs, MT: Summit University Press. Pgs 14, 15, 34, 46, 57, 66, 107, 220-230.

23. Hargis, David M. 1996. "Yeshua the Messiah." <u>Messianic Bureau International</u>.
    [http://www.messianic.com/articles/yeshua.htm].

24. Kox, Norbert H. 2002. "Exposition on the Names Yesu-Yahweh and Jesus." <u>Jehovah, Apoclypse House.com</u>.
    [http://www.nhkox.homestead.com/who1.html].

25. Swami Abhedananda. 2000. From "Swami Abhedananda's Journey into Kashmir and Tibet," by Ansupati Dasgupta and Kunja Kundu of the Ramakrishn "The Tomb of Jesus." <u>Vendanta Math Publication Dept</u>. Calcutta, India.
    [http://www.tombofjesus.com/mpswam.htm].

26. Chodron, Thubten. 2003. <u>Buddhism for Beginners</u>. Ithaca, NY: Snow King Publishing, pg 59.

27. Bramley, William. 1989. <u>The Gods of Eden.</u> New York: Avon, pg 132.

28. Aubuchon, Jr., R. 1982. "God, Who Is He? El Shaddai." <u>RFPT Sermons.com</u>.
    [http://www.rfptsermons.com/god7.html].

29. Ze'er Herzog. 1999. "Yahweh Had a Wife?" <u>Ha'aertz, Disinformation</u>.
    [http://www.disinfo.com/site/printarticle651.html].

30. Lilinah biti-Anat. "The Deity Temple - Room Two. The Deities in the Myths of Ugarit." Qadash Kanahnu. 1990-1997. [http://www.geocities.com/SoHo/Lofts/2938/mindei.html].

31. Geerts, L.C. "The Religion of Babylonia and Assyria." Earth-History.com. 1998-2006. [http://www.earth-history.com/Babylonian/bab-gods.htm].

32. "Phoenician Canaanite Religion–Pagan." Encyclopedia Phoenicia. 2003. [http://www.phoenicia.org/pagan.html].

33. Drudge, Matt. 2003. "How it all went down: detailed report of Bush's secret trip." The Drudge Report. [http://www.drudgereport.com/flashbb.html].

34. Islahi, Amin Ashan. 2004. "Tawheed, Oneness of God." Understanding Islam. [http:www.understandingislam.com].

35. Van Natten, Stephen. 1995. "Chapter Fourteen: Al Hajj Ya Allah." BlessedQuietness.com. [http://www.blessedquietness.com/alhaj/page14.htm].

36. Shamoun, Sam. "Allah of Islam, IS He Yahweh, God of the Bible?" Answering Islam. 1999-2006. [http://www.answeringislam.org/responses/Abualrub/Allahs_identy.htm].

37. "Allah - the Moon God." Biblebelievers.com. 1997-1998. Yeshua Communications Network. [http://www.biblebelievers.org/au/moongod.htm].

38. Freeman, Colin. 2003."Iraqis Celebrate Hussein's Capture with a Burst of Gunfire Across the Land." San Francisco Chronicle. [http://www.sfgate.com/cgi-bin/article.cg?file=/c/a/2003/12/15/MNGHMENGSPI.DTL].

39. Kinnaer, Jacques. 2004. "The Narmer Palette." The Ancient Egypt Site. [http://www.ancient-egypt.org/index.html].

40. "The Narmer Palette." (Observation of Replica of the Narmer Palette). Carnegie Museum of Pittsburgh. Egypt Room Display. 2006.

41. Gardner, Laurence. 2002. <u>Genesis of the Grail Kings</u>. Gloucester, MA: Fairwinds Press.

42. Kimball, Charles Scott. 2006. Trans. E.A. Wallis Dudge. "The Negative Confessions from the Papyrus of Ani. The Declaration of Innocence from the Book of the Dead." <u>The Xenophile Historian</u>. [http://www.nefertiti.webland.com/negativeconfessions/index.html].

43. Crystal, Ellie. "Egyptian Book of the Dead 1240 BC Papyrus of Ani." <u>Crystalinks.com</u>. 1995-2006. [http://www.crystalinks.com/egyptafterlife.html].

44. Nehring, Arlene K. 2003. "The Ten Commandments: A Sign of God's Covenant with Israel." <u>Eden Church</u>. United Eden Church of Christ. 23. . [http://www.edenucc.com/sermons/20030323.html?word].

45. Shaked, Edith. 2006. "The Nature and Central Themes of Judaism. <u>The Exodus and Giving of the Torah, 1300 BC</u>. University of Arizona. [http://www.u.arizona.edu/~shaked/Judaism/Judaism.html].

46. Crystal, Ellie. "Sumerian Calendars and Astronomy Sumerian Science, Religion, Culture." <u>Crystalinks.com</u>. 1995-2006. [http:www.crystalinks.com/sumercalendars.html].

47. Crystal, Ellie. "Sumerian Art and Architecture." <u>Crystalinks.com</u>. 1995-2006. [http://www.crystalinks.com/sumerart.html].

48. "Sumerian Names of the Gods." <u>The Niburian Council Translated into 12 Languages</u>. 1999. [http://www.bibliotecapleyades.net/sitchin/names_gods.html]. Taken from [http://www.geocities.com/elchasqui_2index1.html].

49. Heron, Patrick. 2005. <u>The Nephilim and the Pyramid of the Apocalypse</u>. Longwood, FL: Xulon Press, pg 11.

50. "History of Giza." <u>NOVA Online Adventure</u>. 1997. Public Broadcasting Service.
[http://www.pbs/org.wgbh/nova/pyramid/explore/gizahistory].

51. Ward, Daniel Sewell. 2005. "Sodom and Gomorrah." <u>Library of Halexandria</u>.
[http:www.halexandria.org/dward194.htm].

52. Quayle, Steve, and David Hatcher Childress, 2006. "Technology of the Gods: the Incredible Sciences of the Ancients." "The Evidence for Ancient Atomic Warfare: Part 2." <u>Welcome to the World of Steve Quayle</u>. Adventures Unlimited Press.
[http://www.stevequayle.com/Giants/Ancient.Civ_technol/ancient.warfare.pts.html].

53. Wood, Bryant. 1995. "Is there any evidence for the Biblical story of Sodom and Gomorrah's destruction by fire and brimstone (sulfur)?" <u>Christian Answers.Net</u>. Associates for Biblical Research.
[http://www.christiananswers.net/q-abr-a007.html].

54. "Sodom and Gomorrah Rediscovered. The Story of Sodom and Gomorrah." <u>Bible Plus</u>. 1992-2003. The Bible Research Company.
[http://www.bibleplus.org/discoveries/sodomfound.htm].

55. "Genesis 19: Sodom and Gomorrah." <u>Cygnus' Study Debunking the Bible.</u> 2006. [http://www.cygnus-study.com/page8.html].

56. Dollinger, Andre Reshafim. 2000. "Israel. 12th Dynasty, C.1991-1786 B.C.E. An Inroduction to the History and Culture of Pharoanic Egypt Dynasties XII to XVII, the Growth of the Middle Class and the Conquest of the Hyksos." <u>Ancient Egypt Online</u>.
[http://nefertiti.iwebland.com/history12-17.htm].

57. See note 56 above.

58. Fox, Troy. "Who Were the Hyksos ?" <u>Tour Egypt</u>. 1996-2005. Egyptian Ministry of Tourism. [http://www.touregypt.net/featurestories/hyksos.htm].

59. <u>The Trinity Report.</u> 1997. Trinity Consulting. [http://www.direct.ca/trinity/duel.html].

60. Kirby, Peter. "The Protevangelium of James." *Early Christian Writings*. 2001-2006. [http://www.earlychristianwriting.com/infancyjames.html].

61. Rhys, Jocelyn. 1990. "Shaken Creeds: The Virgin Birth Doctrine." <u>An English Atheist</u>. [http://englishatheist.org/index.shtml].

62. Book Review by Joan d'Arc. 2004. "Sons of God: Krishna, Buddha and Christ Unveiled." <u>Acharya S. Adventures Unlimited</u>. Paranoia: The Conspiracy and Paranormal Reader. [http://www.paranoiamagazine.com/bookreviews.html].

63. "DNA Study, Neanderthals Not Human Ancestors." <u>VNN VAISHNAVA News World</u>. 2003. [http://www.unm.org/world/wd0003].

64. See note 10 above, pg 187.

65. "Key Suspect in Madrid Bombings Had Al Qaeda Ties." Morning Edition. <u>NPR News</u>. 2004. [http://www.npr.org/templates/story/story.phy?storyid=1767742].

66. Poggioli, Sylvia. 2004. "New Spanish Leader Vows to Pull Iraq Troops." Morning Edition. <u>NPR News</u>. [http://www.npr.org/templates/story/story.phy?storyid=1766503].

67. "Physical Description of Jesus, the Oldest Views and Literary Data on the External Appearance of Jesus." <u>The Nazarene Way of Essenic Studies. 2006.</u> [http://www.thenazareneway.com/likeness_of_our_saviour.htm].

68. See note 22 above, at 219.

69. See note 68 above.

70. King, L.W. Trans. "From the Seven Tablets of Creation." London. Enuma Elish, The Epic of Creation. 1902." Sacred Texts.com. 2006. Internet Sacred Text Archive. [http://www.sacred-texts.com/ane/enuma.htm].

71. Ward, Daniel Sewell. 2003. "Lilith, Handmaiden to Inanna." Library of Halexandria. [http://www.halexandria.org/dward184.htm].

72. "Antediluvian King Lists, Kings Before the Flood." People in History, Mythology and Folklore. Connections of Chaos. 2003. [http://www.b17.com/family/lwp/ged2htm/d0035/l6.html].

73. "Sexagesimal, Babylonian Numerals, Historical Weights and Measures." Teachers Paradise.com. 2006. [http://www.teachersparadise.com/ency/en/wikipedia/s/se/sexagesimal.html].

74. Hazelwood, Mark. 2004. "Subject: Planet X From A Biblical Perspective. Why Is NASA Silent on PX?" The Survival Center. [http://www.survivalcenters.com/planaetx072804.html].

75. "Global Warming on Mars?" Current Science and Technology Center. 2001. [http://www.mos.org/est/article/80/9.html].

76. Hogan, Jenny. 2003. "Sun More Active Than for a Millenium." New Scientist.com. New Scientist Print Edition. [http://www.newscientist.com/article.ns?id=dn4321].

77. Dume, Belle. 2003. "Solar Activity Reaches New High." Physics Web. [http://www.physicsweb.org/articles/news/7/12/2].

78. Philips, Tony. 2003. "The Sun Goes Haywire." NASA News. [http://science.nasa.gov/headlines/y2003/12nov_haywire.html].

79. See note 10 above, pg 318-19.

80. "Neolithic Period." <u>Infoplease, Encyclopedia</u>. 2005. Columbia Electronic Encyclopedia, 6th Edition. Columbia University Press. [http://www.infoplease.com/ce6/society/A0835205.html].

81. See note 80 above.

82. Ward, Daniel Sewell. 2003. "Nibiru ala Kepler." <u>The Library at Halexandria</u>. Annals of Earth. Interlude 1. [http://www.halexandria.org/dward799.htm].

83. Kimball, Glenn. 2005. "The Kolbrin, Ancient Warnings, Modern Threats." <u>Yowbooks.com</u>. [http://www.yowbooks.com/html/Kolbrin.html].

84. Sitchin, Zecharia. 1976. *The 12th Planet*. New York: Avon, 362-386.

85. "Explanation About Evolution and Reincarnation of the Spirit. All about the Gift of Reincarnation, the Path for the Evolution of Spirit through Many Lives." <u>The Third Testament</u>. 2005. The 144000 Foundation. [http://www.144000.net/reincarnation/index_2.htm].

86. "The Epitaph of Young Ben Franklin." <u>The Franklin Institute Museum</u>. 2006. [http://www.fi.edu/franklin/timeline/epitaph.html].

87. Shri Adi Shakti. 2000. "Reincarnation Quotes from Famous People." <u>The Kingom of God</u>. [http://www.adishakti.org/_/reincarnation_quotes_from_famous_people].

88. Taylor, Humphrey. 2003. "The Religious and Other Beliefs of Americans." <u>Harris Interactive</u>. [http://www.harrisinteractive.com/harris_poll/index.asp?PID=359].

89. Slick, Michael J. "Was John the Baptist Really Elijah?" *<u>Christian Apologetics and Research Ministry.</u>* 1995-2006. [http://www.carm.org>].

90. "Lady Fatima, Brief Biography of Lady Fatimah (A.S.) The Daughter of the Last Messenger (saaw.) and the Mother of the Imams." <u>Global Islamic Web Ring</u>. 2006.
[http://www.convertstoislam.com/Fatima/fatima.html].

91. Terelya, Josyp. 2005. "One More Secret About Fatima." <u>The Fatima Center</u>.
[http://www.fatima.org/crusader/cr40/cr40pg24.asp].

92. Contents and Editing by Lishtar. 2000. "Mesopotamian Religion and Magic. Adapa's Treatise on Sumerian Religion." <u>Gateways to Babylon</u>.
[http://www.gatewaystobabylon.com/religion/sumrel1.html].

93. Swami Nirmalananda Giri. 2006. "May a Christian Believe in Reincarnation?" <u>Atma Joyoti Ashram Spiritual Writings</u>.
[http://www.atmajyoti.org/saw_xtian_believe_rein.asp].

94. Cronshaw, Allan. 2006. "Why Do Modern Christians Reject the Doctrine of the Pre-Existent Soul That Evolves to Perfection over Many Lifetimes?" <u>Ebionite Restoration-Christian Renewal</u>.
[http://ebionite.com/reincarnation.htm].

95. "Resurrection." <u>Answers.Com</u>. 2006. Columbia Encyclopedia. Columbia University Press.
[http://www.answers.com/topic/resurrection].

96. "Christian Reincarnating." <u>The Reluctant Messenger</u>. 2002. Internet Innovations, Inc.
[http://www.reluctantmessenger.com/origen3.html].

97. Lambdin, Thomas O. Transl. 2006. "The Gospel of Thomas." <u>The Nag Hammadi Library</u>. The Gnostic Society Library.
[http://www.webcom.com/gnosis/naghamm/gthlamb.html].

98. See note 96 above.

99. "Reincarnation, Pros and Cons. 4.3 Council of Constantinople

Rejected Pre-existence of Souls and Thus, By Implication, Reincarnation." <u>Vedic Knowledge Online</u>. 2006 [http://www.veda.harekrsna.cz/encyclopedia/reincarnation.htm].

100. Abdullah, Osama. "Islam, the True Religion of God Almighty. What Does Islam Think About Reincarnation?" <u>AnsweringChristianity.com.</u> 2001-2006. [http://www.answering-christianity.com/reincarnation.htm].

101. Schroeder, Tom. 1999. <u>Old Souls and the Scientific Evidence for Past Lives</u>. New York: Simon & Shuster.

102. Abdullah, Osama. "Islam, the True Religion of God Almighty. Psalm 22 and Psalm 88 Confirm That Jesus Never Got Crucified." <u>Answering Christianity.com</u>. 2001-2006. [http://www.answering-christianity.com/psalm_22.htm].

103. Shand, Richard. 1999. "The Empty Tomb. 8th Watch." <u>The Real Jesus.</u> Illuminations. [http://www.mystae.com/ restricted/reflections/messiah/tomb.html].

104. "The Sumerian Civilization Part 2." <u>Lani and Rudy's World</u>. 2001-2005. [http://www.strayreality.com/lanis_strayeality/sumerian_civilization %202.htm].

105. Crystal, Ellie. "Sumerian Gods and Goddesses." <u>Crystalinks.</u> 1995-2006. [http://www.crystalinks.com/sumergods.html].

106. Smith, Gordon. 2000. "Part 39: Jesus Ascends to Heaven. The Story of Jesus. Spring AD 30, A Harmony of the New Testament." Trans. J.B. Phillips. <u>Christian Classics Ethereal Library</u>. Calvin College. [http://www.ccel.org/bible/phillips/ CH194NEWBEGINNINGS.htm].

107. Hinrichs, Stephen. 1998. "Resurrection of Jesus Puzzle." <u>Steve Hinrichs Rational Site with a Meaningful Purpose</u>. [http://members.aol.com/SHinrichs9/rssrdeb.htm].

108. "Harmonization of the Visit to Jesus' Tomb." <u>Rational Christianity</u> 2005. Christian Apologetics.
[http://www.rationalchristianity.net/jesus.tomb.html]

109. Sitchin, Zecharia. 1995. *Divine Encounters: A Guide to Visions, Angels and Other Emissaries.* New York: Avon, 369.

110. See note 109 above.

111. Smith, Gordon. 2000. "Appearances of Jesus After His Resurrection. The Story of Jesus. Spring AD30, A Harmony of the New Testament." Trans. J.B. Phillips. <u>Christian Classics Ethereal Library</u>. Calvin College. [http://www.ccel.org/bible/phillips/ CH194NEWBEGINNINGS.htm].

112. Borg, Marcus. 2000. "The Ascension of Jesus." <u>Seeing the Bible Again.</u>
[http://beliefnet.com/story/25/story_2587_1.html].

113. Trotter, Jr. Andrew H. 1997. "Ascension of Jesus." <u>Crosswalk.com</u>. Baker's Evangelical Dictionary of Theology. [http://bible.crosswalk.com/Dictionaries/ BakersEvangelicalDictionary/bed.cgi].

114. See note 109 above, pg 54-59.

115. Cooke, Patrick. "Flying Vehicles and Advanced Technology In the Bible." <u>The Bible UFO Connection</u>. 1997-2004. Oracle Research Institute. [http://www.bibleufo.com].

116. "Part IV – the Life and Teachings of Jesus. Paper 168 – The Resurrection of Lazurus." <u>The Urantia Book</u>. 1955. The Urantia Foundation. [http://www.urantia.org/papers/paper168.html].

117. "President Bush Discusses Early Transfer of Iraqi Sovereignty." <u>The White House</u>. 2004.
[http://www.whitehouse.gov/news/releases/ 2004/06/200406280-9.html].

118. Pratt, David. 1997. "Heaven and Hell." Exploring Theosophy, the Synthesis of Science, Religion and Philosophy.
[http://ourworld.compuserve.com/homepages/DP5/heaven.htm].

119. "What is Heaven Like, Is There Really a Heaven?"
Every Student.Com. 2006.
[http://www.everystudent.com/sg/forum/heaven2.html].

120. Price, Robert M., and Reginald Finley Sr. 2006. "Is Heaven the Sky?"
Heaven and Its Wonders, and Earth: The World the Biblical Writers Thought they Lived In.
[http://www.infidelguy.com/heaven_sky.htm].

121. See note 109 above.

123. Miller, David Lee, and Lisa Porteus. 2004. "Saddam Refuses to Sign Charges." Fox News.com.
[http://www.foxnews.com/story/0,2933,124383,00.html].

124. Sitchin, Zecharia. 1998. "The God Who Returned From Heaven."
The Cosmic Code. Excerpts from Elchasqui Web site;
The Earth Chronicles.
[http://www.bibleotcapleyades.net/sitchin/sitchinbooks6_5.html].

125. "Prayer Experiments." Prison Fellowship. 2003. Paraphrased with permission from Prison Fellowship Ministries.
[www.prisonfellowship.org].

126. Timms, Moira. 1998. "Seven Stars (Beyond Prophecies and Predictions.)" Bible Prophecy Research.
[http://philologos.org/bpr/files/s004.htm].

127. Lloyd, Andrew. 2000. "The Dark Star Theory." DawnRazor's Vault.
[http://www.theoldpath.com/dds1.htm].

128. Lloyd, Andrew. 2005. "Nibiru, The Solution." Timeless Voyager Press.
[http://www.darkstar1.co.uk/solution.html].

References

129. "Planet X Hitting Our Primitive Earth." Xfacts.Com. 2006.
[http://xfacts.comx3.htm].

130. "The Search for Planet X, Interview At NASA About Planet
X." *X Facts.Com*. 2006. [http://xfacts.comx3.htm]

131. See note 130 above.

132. See note 10 above, pg 52-59.

133. See note 10 above, pg 52-59.

134. See note 10 above, pg 52-59.

135. Resenmut. 2003. "How Can Comets Show Us Planet X?"
Bad Astronomy and Universe Today Forum.
[http://www.bautforum.com/archive/indes.php/t10019.htm].

136. Foard, James M. 2004. "The Untold Story of Charles Darwin." From
the Nebulis Hypothesis, A Study of the Historical and Philosophical
Implications of Darwinian Theory. The Darwin Papers.
[http://www.thedarwinpapers.com/oldsite/number1/
Darwinpapers1Htm.ht].

137. Stroebel, Lee. 2000. *The Case for Faith*. Grand Rapids, MI:
Zondervan Publishing.

138. See note 137 above.

139. Ward, Daniel Sewell. 2006. "The Evolution of Life, 4.0 Billion
B.C.E." The Library of Halexandria.
[http://www.halexandria.org/dward724.htm].

140. Eastman, Mark, and Chuck Missler. 1996. "The Creator Beyond
Space and Time." The Origin of Information. Trinity Consulting.
[http://www.direct.ca/trinity/origin2.html].

141. See note 140 above.

142. See note 10 above, pg 230.

143. Martin, Rick. 2006. "The Names of the Gods, From the Niburian Council of Twelve. Translated into 12 languages." <u>Bibliote Capleyades</u>. [http://www.bibliotecapleyades.net/sitchin/names_gods.html].

144. See note 84 above, pg 89-90, 290.

145. See note 84 above, pg 89-90, 290.

146. See note 84 above, pg 89-90, 290.

147. See note 105 above.

148. Temple, Robert. 1998. *The Sirius Mystery*. Rochester, VT: Destiny Books. 118.

149. See note 10 above, pg 230.

150. See note 10 above.

151. Namaste & Sita Ram. 2006. "The Concept of Ages in Hinduism." <u>Punditravi.com</u>. [http://punditravi.com/concept_of_ages_in_hinduism.htm].

152. Sitchin, Zecharia. 2002. <u>The Lost Book of Enki: Memoirs and Prophecies of an Extraterrestrial God</u>. Rochester, VT: Bear and Company, pg 103-4.

153. "The Face On Mars." <u>Malin Space Science Systems.</u> 1995. [http://www.msss.com/education/facepage/face.html].

154. "Babylonian Creation of Man." <u>Ancient Mesopotamia and the Near East</u>. 2002. [http://www.geocities.com/garyweb65/creationm2.html].

155. See note 154 above.

References

156. "Atrahasis I Creation of Humans." <u>Grand Valley State University</u>. 2005.
[http://faculty.gvsu.edu/websterm/Atrahasi.htm].

157. y de la Torre, Mattfeld, and Warttig Walter Reinhold. 2001. "The Tree of Knowledge of Good and Evil and the Tree of Life in the Garden of Eden." <u>Bible Origins</u>.
[http://www.homestead.com/bibleorigins*net/
edenstreeofknowledgelife.html].

158. See note 157 above.

159. See note 157 above.

160. See note 10 above, pg 20, 22, 186.

161. Martin, Rick. 1999. "Great Zulu Shaman and Elder, Credo Mutwa. On Alien Abduction & Reptiles." <u>Metatech</u>. The Spectrum Magazine.
[http://www.metatech.org/credo_mutwa.html].

162. Collins, Debra. "Prevalence of Genetic Conditions / Birth Defects. Genetics Education Center." 1995-2006. <u>University of Kansas Medical Center</u>.
[http://www.kumc.edu/gec/prof/prevalnc.html].

163. Sagan, Carl. 1980. <u>Cosmos</u>. New York: Random House 17.

164. Kimball, John W. 2006. "Telomeres, Telomeres and Cellular Aging, Telomerase." <u>Kimball's Biology Pages</u>.
[http://users.rcn.com/jkimball.ma.ultranet/BiologyPages/T/Telomeres.html].

165. See note 152 above.

166. See note 152 above.

167. Dankebring, William F. 2006. "Cain and Abel and the Seduction of Eve." <u>Triumph Prophetic Ministries.</u> Church of God.
[http://www.triumphpro.com/cain_and_abel_and_the_seduction_ofeve.htm].

168. "The Land of Nod." Wikipedia 2006. Offered to the public under the GNU free download license. [http://en.wikipedia.org/wiki/Land_of_Nod].

169. y de la Torre, Mattfeld, and Warttig, Walter Reinhold. 2001. "The Garden of Eden not Aden in the Yemin, but Wadi Adhana/Dhana at Marib?" Bible Origins. [http://www.homestead.com/bibleorigins*net/ edenaghanamarib.html].

170. "Rub al-Khali." The Saudi Arabia Information Resource. 2006. Saudi Arabian Government Ministries. [http://www.saudinf.com/main/a35.htm].

171. Naida, Uthaya. 2006. "Sutric Aryan Invasions." The Bible of Aryan Invasions Volume IV. [http://www.dalitstan.org/books/bibai/bibai4.html].

172. Crystal, Ellie. "Sumerian Architechture, Votive Statues." Crystalinks.com. 1995-2006. [http://www.crystalinks.com/sumerart.html].

173. See note 84 above, pg 370-78, 404-05.

174. See note 84 above, pg 370-78, 404-06.

175. Heron, Patrick. 2005. The Nephilim and the Pyramid of the Apocalypse. Longwood, FL: Xulon Press.

176. See note 175 above.

177. See note 175 above.

178. Daily, H., ed. "80% of the proteins in the human and chimpanzee genomes are different." And God Said, Let Us Make Man in Our Image, After Our Image, After Our Likeness. Genesis Research. [http://www.accuracyingenesis.com/flood.html].

179. Daily, H., ed. "The Biblical Flood." Noah's Flood. Genesis Research.
[http://www.accuracyingenesis.com/flood.html].

180. Hunt, Keith. "Noah's Flood–Universal - #1." Things That May Surprise You. [http://keithhunt.com/Flood1.html].

181. See note 180 above.

182. Neuhaeuser, R., and J.V. Feitzinger. "Mass and orbit estimation of planet X via a family of comets." X Facts Research.com.
[http://www.xfacts.com/planetx_search.html].

183. Irfan, Hwaa. 2002. "The Great Flood and Noah's Ark." ShiaNews.com.
[http://www.shianews.com/low/articles/education/0000304.php].

184. Martell, Jason.. "The Piri Reis Map" (Includes Zeno's Chart Information) Ancient X.com.
[http://www.ancientx.com/nm/anmviewr.asp?a=27&z=1].

185. See note 184 above.

186. Leake, Jonathan. "Giant Comet Launched Noah's Ark." Theory Supporting the Biblical Account of the Great Flood. The Golden Age Project.
[http://www.goldenageproject.org.uk/19giantcomet.html].

187. See note 186 above.

188. "Research Raises Fear of Dramatic Temperature Change During Warming Trend." CNN.com. 1998.
[http://cnn.com/TECH/science/9810/22/warming.trend].

189. "Neolithic Period." Infoplease. 2005. Columbia Electronic Encyclopedia, 6th Edition. Columbia University Press.
[http://www.infoplease.com/ceb/society/a0835205.html].

190. See note 189 above.

191. See note 2 above, pg 154.

192. See note 152 above, pg 269.

193. See note 152 above, pg 269.

194. See note 84 above, pg 412-422.

195. Ward, Daniel, Seward. "Sodom and Gomorrah."
The Halexandria Library.
[http://www/halexandria.com].

196. Sitchin, Zecharia. 1990. The Lost Realms. New York: Avon, 232-233.

197. "The Great Mountain, Sumerian Hymn." Jewel In the Lotus–
Complete Daily Readings. 2004. Zinester Ezine Directory.
[http://www.archives.zinester.com/70603/23686.html].

198. See note 197 above.

199. See note 109 above, pg 295-298.

200. See note 109 above, pg 295-298.

201. See note 109 above, pg 295-298.

202. Moses the Mystery Man." Essays By Ekowa. 2004.
[http://www.essaysbyekowa.com/mosesII.htm].

203. "The Invasion of the Hyksos." Hebrew Peoples In Egypt.
2006.
[http://www.mystae.com/restricted/streams/thera/hapiru.html].

204. See note 203 above.

205. See note 202 above.

206. See note 202 above.

207. "Amenhotep IV (Akhenaton). 1352-1336 BC, 18th Dynasty. The Cult of the Aten." Tour Egypt! 2006. Ministry of Tourism. [http://www.touregypt.net/18dyn10.htm].

208. See note 203 above.

209. Grigor-Scott, Anthony. "Chariot Wheels Found in the Sea." The True Location of the Red Sea Crossing. British Church of God. [http://www.british-israel.ca/redsea.htm].

210. See note 209 above.

211. Wyatt, Ron. 2005. "The Red Sea Crossing." Ark Discovery.com. [http://www.arkdiscovery.com/red_sea_crossing.htm].

212. See note 211 above.

213. Whiston, William, trans. Sage Software, ed. "Book II– From the Death of Isaac to the Exodus Out of Egypt." The Works of Flavious Josephus. Antiquities of the Jews. Christian Classics Ethereal Library. [http://www.ccel.org/j/josephus/JOSEPHUS.HTM].

214. Wyatt, Ron. 2005. "The Blackened Peak of the REAL Mount Sinai Found." The Real Mt. Sinai in Saudi Arabia. [http://www.arkdiscovery.com/mt_sinai_found.htm].

215. See note 214 above.

216. See note 214 above.

217. "Who Wrote the 5 Books of Moses? (aka the Pentateuch, the Books of Law, the Torah)." Ontario Consultants on Religious Tolerance. 2005. [http://www.religioustolerance.org/chr_torn.htm].

218. Billings, Tod. 1999. "Moses Wrote the Torah?" Freethought web.org. Arkansas Society of Free Thinkers.

[http://www.stephenjaygould.org./ctrl/archive/billings_torah.html].

219. Colmer, Hugh. "Meet the Devil in the British Museum." Crosscircle Institute.
[http://www.crosscircle.com/meet%20the%20devil.htm].

220. Morse, Melvin and Paul Perry. 1990. Closer to the Light. New York: Ivy Books.

221. Heron, Patrick. 2005. The Nephilim and the Pyramid of the Apocalypse. Longwood, FL. Xulon Press. 24-5.

222. See note 221 above.

223. "Where Were the Ten Lost Tribes?" Lost Tribes of Israel. 2000. NOVA Online.
[http://www.pbs.org/wgbh/nova/israel/losttribes.html].

224. Sitchin, Zecharia. From Elchasqui Web site. 1998. "The God Who Returned From Heaven." The Cosmic Code. The Harran Inscriptions.
[http://www.bibleotcapleyades.net/sitchin/sitchinbooksb_5.htm].

225. See note 224 above.

226. Dunkin, Timothy. "Some Notes About Almah and Its Translation as Virgin." Study to Answer.Net. 2000-2004.
[http://www.studytoanswer.net/doctrine/almah.html].

227. Abdallah, Yusuf. 1998. "Mary and Jesus are a Sign." Jesus Gives Peace, Jesus in the Qur'an and the Bible. Al Injil.
[http://www.injil.org/Peace/c5.htm].

228. "Over 300 Prophecies Foretold Jesus / Yeshua as the Jewish Messiah." BibleProbe.com.
[http://bibleprobe.com/300great.htm].

229. Condarcuri, Vincent. "Daniel's Prophecy 9:24-27." End of Times.
[http://www.geocities.com/daniel999_ca/].

230. "The Book of Daniel, Chapter 9." Eschatology in the Prophecies of Daniel.
[http://www.csg.net/eschatology/Daniel-9.htm].

231. See note 228 above.

232. "The Influence of Christianity And Christian Apocryphal Books."
The Original Sources of the Qur'an, Chapter IV. The Interactive Bible.
[http://www.bible.ca/islam/library/Tisdall/Sources/chap4.htm].

233. De Young, Arnold. "What Was the Star of Bethlehem?"
Christianswers.net.
[http://www.christianswers.net/q-eten/edn-c018.html].

234. Kigdar, Mark. 2000. "Star of Bethlehem." The Museum of Unnatural History.
[http://www.unmuseum.org/bstar.htm].

235. Ward, Daniel Sewell. 2005.
"Age of Pisces." The Library of Halexandria.
[http://www.Halexandria.org/dward207.htm].

236. Coffman, James Burton. "There Came Wisemen….
"We Saw His Star in the East …." Study Light.org.
[http://studylight.org/com/bcc/view.cgi?book=mt&chapter=002].

237. Suter, Keith. 2004. "Mystery of the Magi and Mary's Boy Child."
Persian Journal.
[http://iranian.ws/cgibin/iran_news/exec/view.cgi/2/5077/printer].

238. Michaels, Henry D 1988. "When Was Jesus Born?" Frequently Asked Questions. Antipas Foundation.
[http://www.antipas.net/2faq.htm].

239. Dankenburg, William F. "When Was Christ Born?" Triumph
     Prophetic Ministries.
     [http://www.triumphpro.com/when_was_jesus_christ_born.htm].

240. Short, Michael L. "MIGDAL EDER." Mayim Hayim
     Ministries. [http://www.mayimhayim.org/
     Rabbi%20Mike/Migdal%20Eder.htm].

241. Keifer, James. "Part Two, Massacre of the Innocents." The Infancy
     Narratives in Matthew and Luke. The CHRISTIA Library.
     [http://elvis.rowan.edu/~kilroy/CHRISTIA/library/infancy2.html].

242. "Massacre of the Innocents." Massacre of the Innocents Articles and
     News from Start Learning Now. Start Learning Now.
     [http://www.startlearningnow.com/
     articles/massacre-of-the-innocents.htm].

243. Murphy, Frederick J. 2005. "Circumstantial Evidence." America The
     National Catholic Weekly. [http://www.americanmagazine.org/
     BookReview.cfm?articletypeid=31&textid=4046&issueid=520].

244. "Ambrosius Theodosius Macrobius." Wikipedia.
     [http://en.wikipedia.org/wiki/macrobius].

245. Tierney, John J. Potter, and Douglas J. 2003. Trans. "Herod the
     Great." The Catholic Encyclopedia Volume VII, Online Edition by K.
     Knight.
     [http://www.newadvent.org/cathen/07289c.htm].

246. See note 245 above.

247. Hulsman, Cornelis. 2003. "The Holy Family in Egypt." Al Ahram
     Weekly On Line. 25-31.
     [http://weekly.ahram.org.eg/2003/670/tr3.htm].

248. "Buddhism in Christianity." The Hindu Universe.
     Hindunet.
     [http://www.hindunet.org/alt_hindu/1995_May_2/msg0015.html].

249. See 248 above.

250. Gaborro, Allen. 1997. Reviewed by Marcus Borg. "Jesus and Buddha, Parallel Sayings." Ulysses Press. Eclectica Book Reviews.
[http://www.eclectica.org/v2n3/gaborro.html].

251. See note 250 above.

252. de Lubricz, Rene Schwallor and David Sewell Ward. 2006. "Gospel of Thomas." The Library at Halexandria.
[http://www.halexandria.org/dward748.htm].

253. Shand, Richard. 1999. "The Ministry of Jesus." The Real Jesus. Illuminations.
[http://www.mystae.com/restricted/reflections/messiah/ministry.html.

254. See note 253 above.

255. See note 253 above.

256. Research by Ajae. 2000. "The Birth of John the Baptist." Mandaean World.
[http://www.geocities.com/mandaeans/birth4.html?20526].

257. Tobin, Paul N. "Jesus and John the Baptist." The Rejection of Pascal's Wager.
[http://www.geocities.com/paulntobin/baptism.html?20058].

258. See note 257 above.

259. See note 22 above.

269. See note 22 above.

261. Keathley, Hampton, IV. 2005. "The Parables in the Olivet Discourse (Matthew 25)." Bible.Org. Liberty University.
[http://bible.org/page.php?page_id=1045]

262. Pardue, Steve D. 1993. "Jesus' Teachings Concerning His Second Coming." The Contents of Prophecy.
[http://www.cynet.com/jesus/Prophecy/teaching.htm].

263. Lahaye, Tim. 1999. Revelation Unveiled.
Grand Rapids, MI: Zondervan Publishing.

264. See note 263 above.

265. See note 263 above.

266. Ward, Daniel Sewell. 2003 "Age of Pisces." The Library of Halexandria.
[http://www.Halexandria.org/dward207.htm].

267. Hogue, John. 1997. "Nostradamus." The Prophets Conference.
[http://www.virtuallystrange.net/ufo/updates/1998/mar/m06-023.shtml].

268. "The End of the World." League of Amateur Games.
[http://www.lagxbl.com/forum/showtread.php?t=5499].

269. "Famine." Wikipedia. Offered to the public under the GNU free download license.
[http://en.wikipedia.org/wiki/famine].

270. Espenak, Fred. 2003. "Solar Eclipses: 2401-2500."
NASA/GODDARD SPACE FLIGHT CENTER.
[http://www.sunearth.gsfc.nasa.gov/eclipse/eclipse.html].

271. Montenegro, Marcia. "The Piscean Avatar, the Jesus of Astrology."
CANA, Christian Answers for the New Age. 1999-2003.
[http://cana.userworld.com/cana_pisean3.html].

272. Mott, Maryann. 2005. "Dogs Used as Shark Bait on French Island."
National Geographic News.
[http://www.nationalgeographic.com].

273. "Human Sacrifice, Chinese Sacrifice, Mesoamerican Sacrifice, Hindu Human Sacrifice, Modern Human Sacrifice." <u>Wikipedia.</u> [http://en.wikipedia.org/wiki/Human_Sacrifice].

274. See note 273 above.

275. "Babylonian Creation of Man." <u>Ancient Mesopotamia and the Near East.</u> 2004. [http://www.geocities.com/garyweb65/creationm2.html].

276. Miller, Glenn M. "The Work Of Christ On The Cross: Sacrifice (OT)" <u>The Christian Thinktank.</u> [http://www.christian-thinktank.com/cross2.html].

277. Sansal, Burak. "The Apostle Paul." <u>All About Turkey</u>. 1996-2005. [http://www.allaboutTurkey.com/paul.htm].

278. Hunt, Randy. 2002. "I Tell You the Truth." <u>Truth Works Devotion.</u> [http://www.truthworks.com/23_August_2002.htm.].

279. Bramley, William. 1990. <u>The Gods of Eden</u>. New York: Avon, Pictures, pg 153.

280. See note 279 above.

281. See note 221 above, pg 194.

Acknowledgements

Old One, Joy DiNardo, and the characters in the story about Iraq are of course, fictional. However, the ancient texts, archaeological evidence, and scientific evidence are not fictional. This is the information from which I derived The Truth. A substantial portion of the ancient history information was taken from Zecharia Sitchin's *Earth Chronicles*. Mr. Sitchin translated ancient Sumerian writings that told of the history of the earth, the gods of Sumer, and the Creation of Man. Also, special credit goes to Elizabeth Clare Prophet for her research on Jesus, from the age of thirteen to age twenty-nine.

Bible quotes are from the *Orthodox Study Bible, New King James Version*, Thomas Nelson Publishers, Nashville, Tennessee, 1993.

It is now up to you to make up your mind.

About the Author

Richard Stabile resides in southwestern Pennsylvania with his family. He is a CPA, and the treasurer of an insurance agency, admittedly not credentials for writing a book determining the Truth about religion and the date of the Second Coming of Jesus.

However, CPAs are trained to think logically, bottom line, and to be unbiased. The Truth was determined by arranging the vast amounts of information that are available in a logical fashion, and then using that information to reach logical conclusions. The hope is for everyone reading *The Second Coming: An Explanation for the Perplexed*, to feel a sense of liberation.